THE TURING TESTS

EXPERT
IQ
PUZZLES

Foreword by Sir Dermot Turing

This edition published in 2019 by Arcturus Publishing Limited
26/27 Bickels Yard, 151–153 Bermondsey Street,
London SE1 3HA

AD006771NT

Printed in the UK

CONTENTS

FOREWORD

Alan Turing's last published paper was about puzzles. It was written for the popular science magazine *Penguin Science News*, and its theme is to explain to the general reader that while many mathematical problems will be solvable, it is not possible ahead of time to know whether any particular problem will be solvable or not.

Alan Turing's role in the development of computers in the mid-twentieth century is well known: perhaps most famously for his invention of the 'Imitation Game' test to determine whether a machine can think. In outline, the test requires a human interrogator to put questions to her subject, which might be a computer or a person, and work out from the responses whether the subject is a real person. If the interrogator concludes that the responses are those of a real person, but it turns out that the subject was in fact a machine, you can say that the machine was 'thinking'. (Alan Turing himself thought that the debate about whether machines could think was rather meaningless – perhaps it was more important to get on and work out what uses the computer could be put to.) Nowadays, a computer program which can imitate a human conversation is not thought particularly 'intelligent', but one which can think up novel ways to solve problems or puzzles is.

Computers are now commonplace, not only in the workplace and on a desk at home, in a smartphone or tablet, but in almost every piece of modern machinery. Teaching people computer skills and coding are now considered obvious elements of the curriculum. Except that this is not so in all parts of the world. In Africa, access to computers in schools is extremely variable, and in some countries there is little or no opportunity for students to have hands-on experience of a real computer. For example, in Malawi, students may have only an 8 per cent chance of using a computer at home, whereas once their school is equipped with computers over 90 per cent of students can get access to what most of us consider to be essential technology. Providing computers motivates students, with 98 per cent saying that learning is more enjoyable when they have the use of a computer.

The Turing Trust, a charity founded by Alan Turing's great-nephew James in 2009, aims to confront these challenges in a practical way which honours Alan Turing's legacy in computer development. The Turing Trust provides still-working, used computers to African schools, enabling computer labs to be built in rural areas where students would otherwise be taught about computers with blackboard and chalk. The computers are refurbished and provided with an e-library of resources relevant to the local curriculum, and then sent out to give a new purpose and bring opportunity to underprivileged communities.

Thank you for buying this book and supporting the Turing Trust.

Sir Dermot Turing
October 2018

To find out more, visit www.turingtrust.co.uk

Notes to the reader
The puzzles in this book are not intended for the faint-hearted, but are designed to challenge experienced puzzle solvers. They are graded in three levels of difficulty, with the puzzles in the third level being truly for experts.

Unless otherwise stated the quotes in the book are by Alan Turing.

The measurements in the book are in metric form, and are often abbreviated (eg m = metres, cm = centimetres and mm = millimetres). Where they are written in full, the book uses UK spellings (as Alan Turing would have done).

	Cube Numbers	Square Numbers	Prime Numbers
1	1	1	2
2	8	4	3
3	27	9	5
4	64	16	7
5	125	25	11
6	216	36	13
7	343	49	17
8	512	64	19
9	729	81	23
10	1000	100	29
11	1331	121	31
12	1728	144	37
13	2197	169	41
14	2744	196	43
15	3375	225	47
16	4096	256	53
17	4913	289	59
18	5832	324	61
19	6859	361	67
20	8000	400	71

Numerical Values of Letters

1	A	26	14	N	13
2	B	25	15	O	12
3	C	24	16	P	11
4	D	23	17	Q	10
5	E	22	18	R	9
6	F	21	19	S	8
7	G	20	20	T	7
8	H	19	21	U	6
9	I	18	22	V	5
10	J	17	23	W	4
11	K	16	24	X	3
12	L	15	25	Y	2
13	M	14	26	Z	1

Playing Card Values

Ace	1	8	8
2	2	9	9
3	3	10	10
4	4	Jack	11
5	5	Queen	12
6	6	King	13
7	7		

Pi (π) = 3.142

1

What number should replace the question mark?

279

6416

12525

21636

3434?

What numbers should replace the question marks?

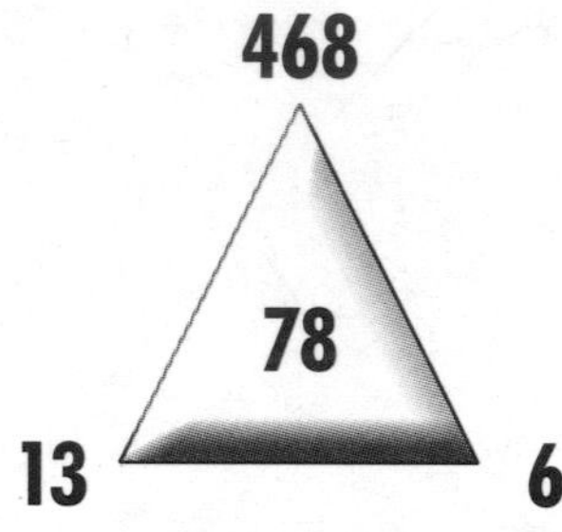

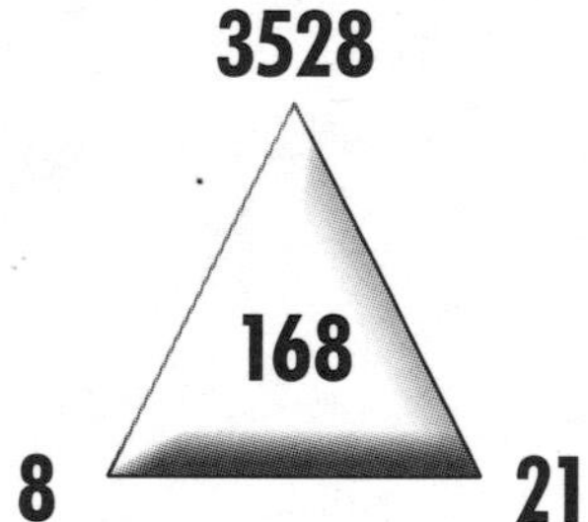

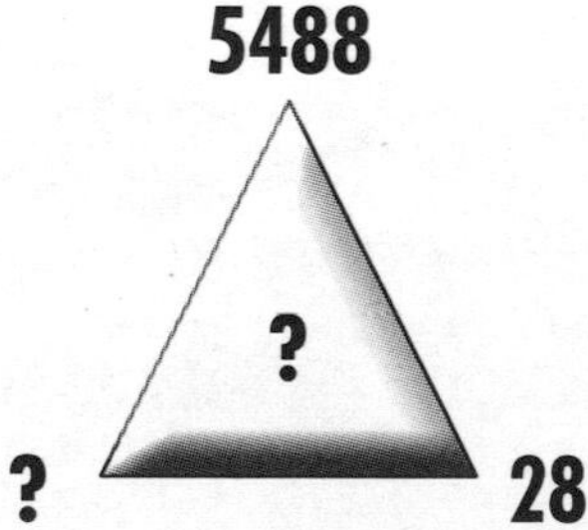

The clock below was correctly set at one o'clock this morning, but it loses four minutes every hour.

The clock now shows the time as 8:30, and was calculated to have stopped at a time two hours before it was checked again this morning.

At what actual time was the clock checked?

'Sometimes it is the people no one can imagine anything of who do the things no one can imagine.'

What is the total surface area of this shape?

Dimensions given are the same at the front as at the back.

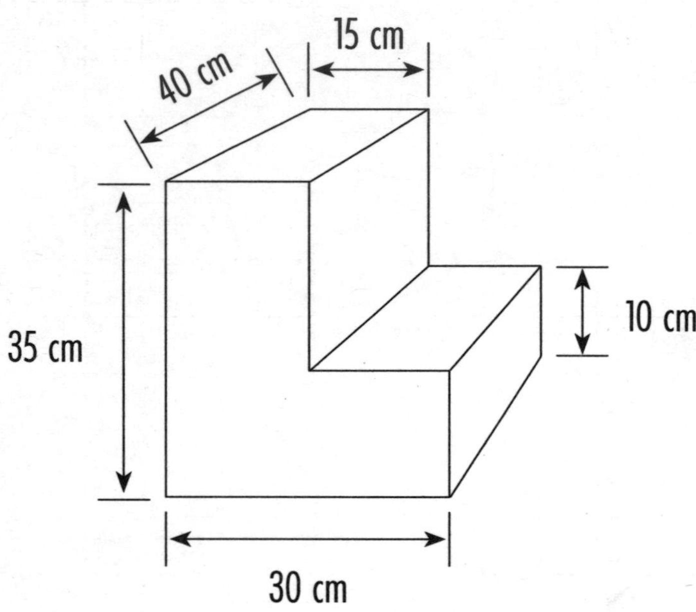

Which of the alternatives (A, B, C, or D) should replace the question mark?

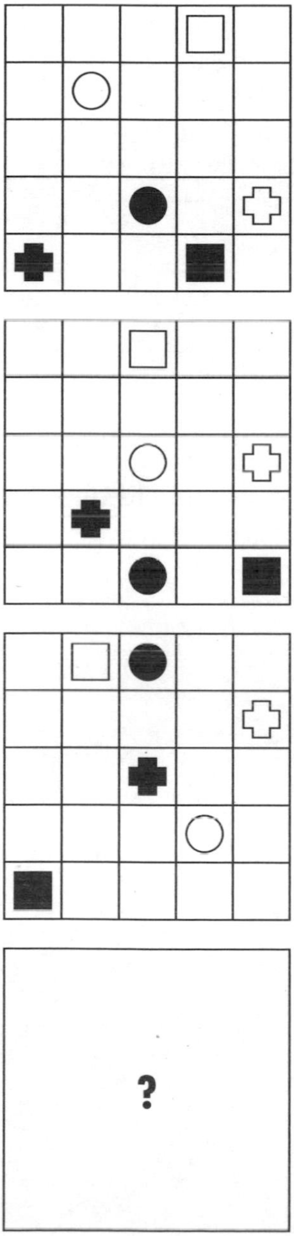

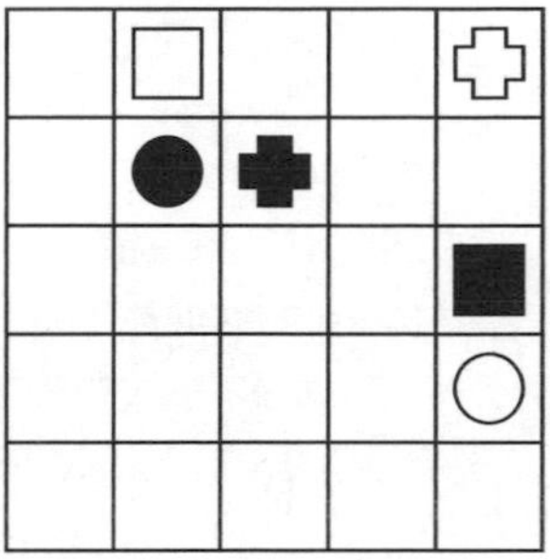

?

A

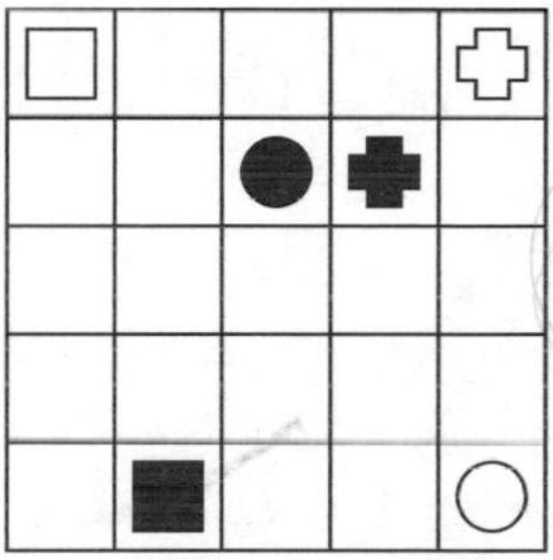

B

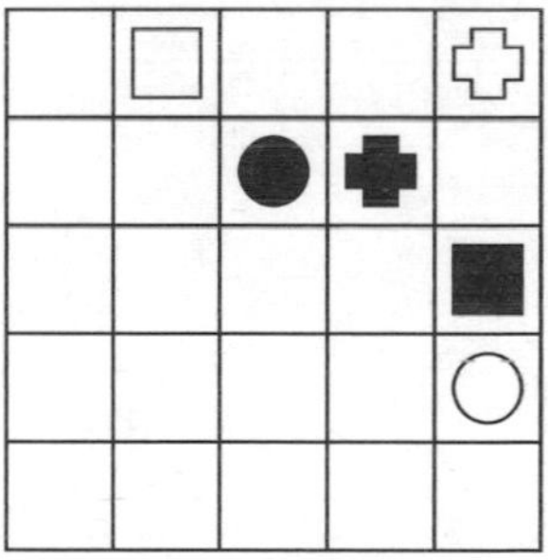

C

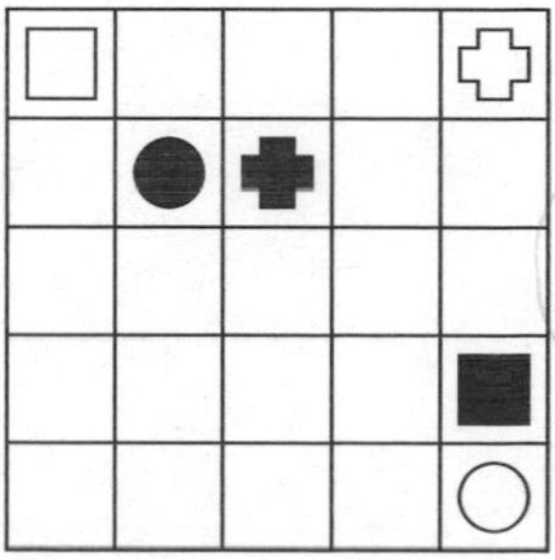

D

Here are three cogs that make moves consecutively: A, B, C, A, B, C, etc.

Cog A can only turn in a clockwise direction, moving one place each turn, so that the arrow points to the next number. If this is an even number, Cog B moves one place clockwise, but if the arrow on Cog A is pointing to an odd number, Cog B moves two places anticlockwise (counterclockwise). If the arrow on Cog B is then pointing to an even number, Cog C moves three places clockwise, but if the arrow on Cog B is pointing to an odd number, then Cog C moves four places anticlockwise (counterclockwise).

Cog A now begins to turn ,and after nine moves of each cog, the arrow on Cog A is pointing to '1' again. What numbers are the arrows pointing to on the other two cogs?

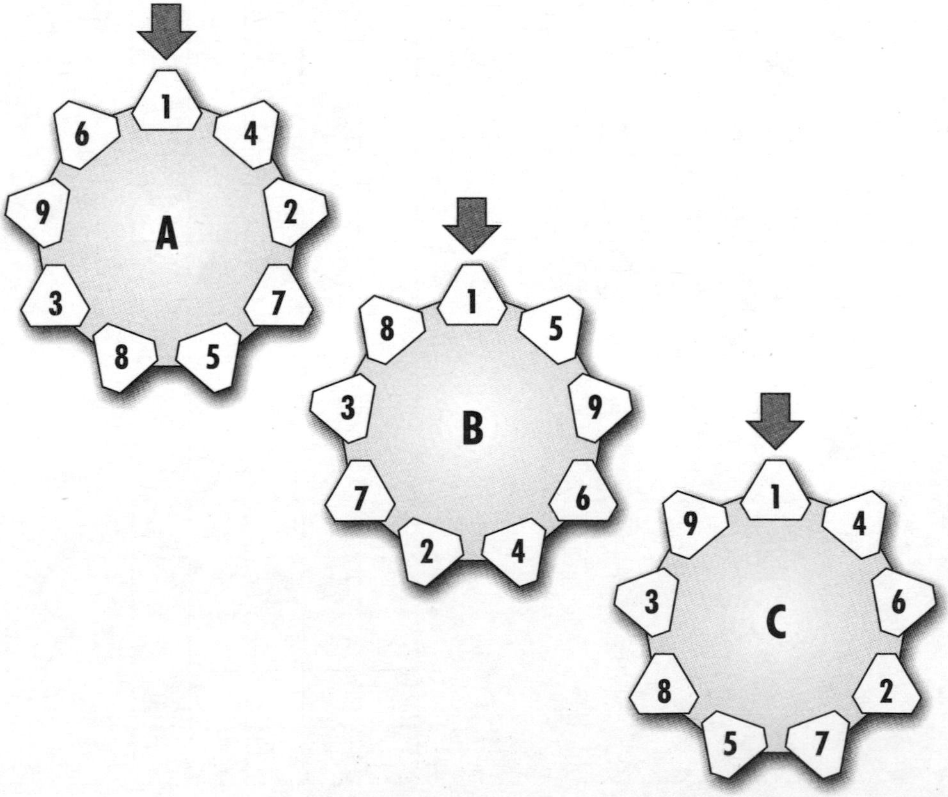

Join all of the dots by drawing lines either horizontally or vertically between them, so that a single loop is formed. The loop may not cross itself or touch at any point. Some lines are already in place.

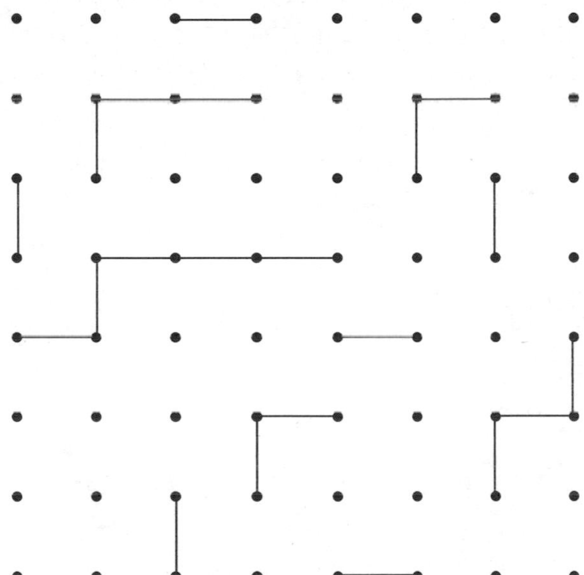

What number should replace the question mark?

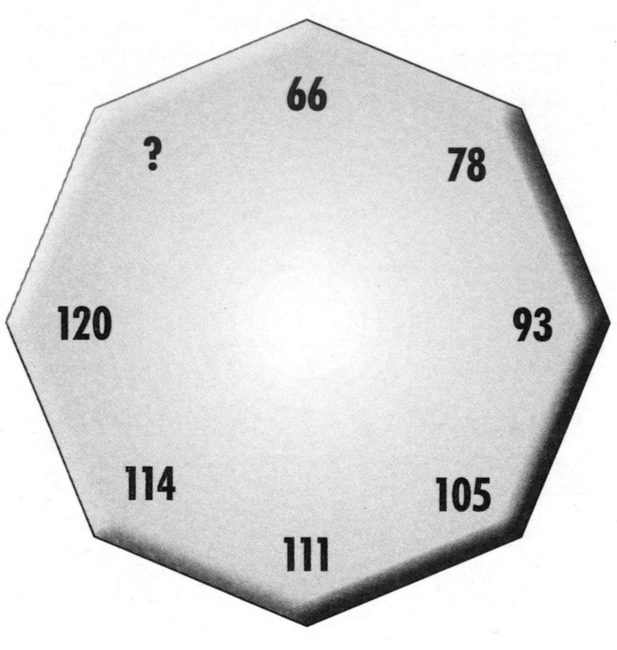

Adam and Eve are fond of exploring ruined houses. Yesterday, they visited one such ruin, a plan of which is below. Only a few walls remain, as you can see.

The walls of the house had been built of perfectly square blocks, the edge of each face measuring exactly two metres, and with some blocks being laid exactly halfway alongside others.

Both decided to walk clockwise around the house, measuring the perimeter of the walls, Adam on the outside, and Eve on the inside, returning to their respective starting points (marked X on the plan).

Excluding the gap of two metres between the first and last blocks, what were the measurements?

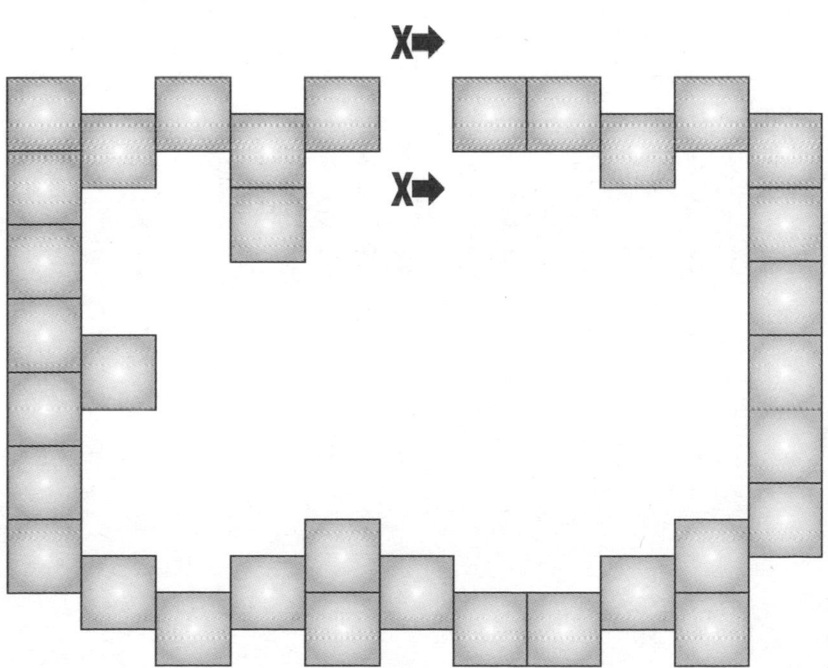

Which is the odd one out?

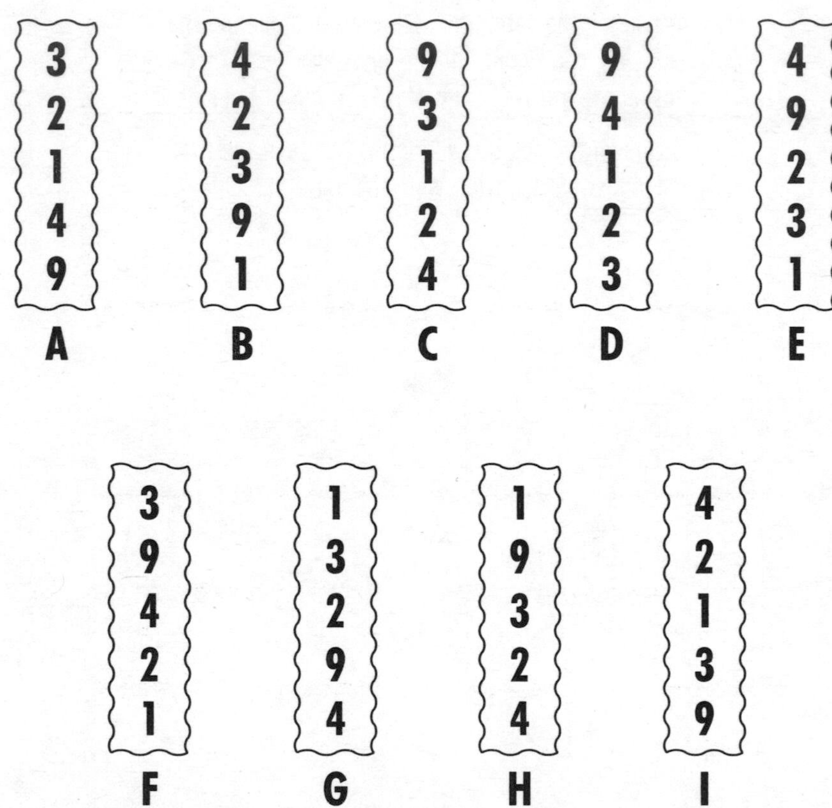

What number should replace the question mark?

Each circle should contain a number that is the sum of the numbers in the two circles beneath it. Fill the missing numbers into the empty circles.

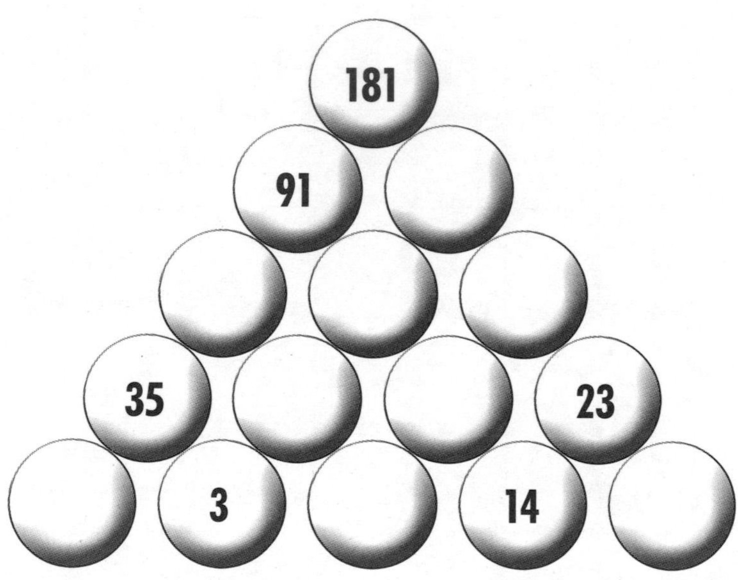

Each can is manufactured from three pieces: one long strip measuring 235 mm x 110 mm forming the body of the can, and two circular end pieces, each with a diameter of 75 mm (which includes the rim of the can).

How many cans can be made from a sheet of metal measuring 675 mm x 770 mm?

Alan Turing showed remarkable ability in Mathematics and Science at Sherborne School in Dorset, South-West England. At the age of 14 he could solve advanced problems without having even studied elementary calculus.

There is a route that can be taken by moving the indicated number of squares as shown by the arrows to arrive at the black square in the middle.

In order to visit every square once only, in which square should you start?

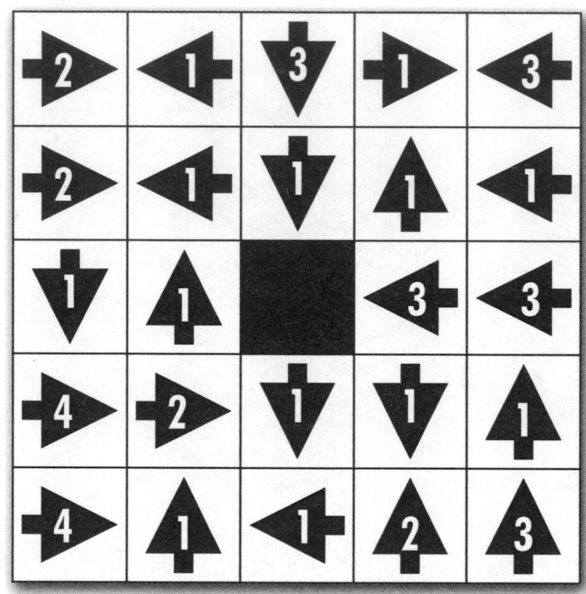

What number should replace the question mark?

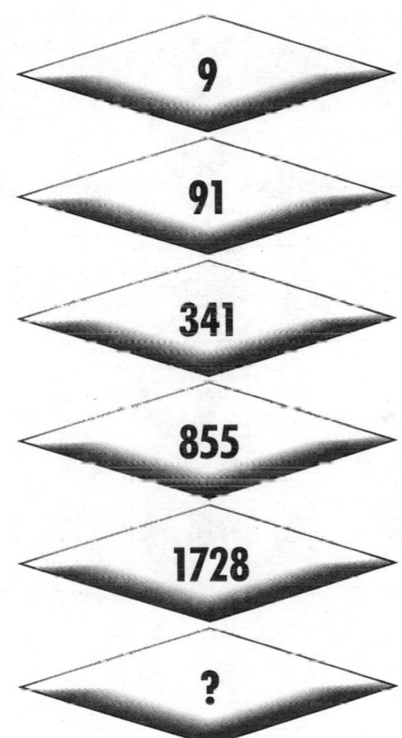

What number should replace the question mark?

7	21	15
8	30	22
12	27	24
28	44	16
22	56	?

Find whole number values for each of the five symbols.

★	✚	▲	●	▲	= 112
▲	★	▲	●	●	= 158
▲	✚	●	▲	▲	= 91
★	✚	●	★	★	= 154
★	■	▲	▲	▲	= 58
=	=	=	=	=	
88	88	137	158	102	

Place circles (representing light bulbs) in some of the empty squares, in such a way that no two bulbs shine on each other, until every square of the grid is lit up. A bulb sends rays of light horizontally and vertically, illuminating its entire row and column unless its light is blocked by a black cell.

Some black cells contain numbers, indicating how many light bulbs are in adjacent squares either immediately above, below, to the right or to the left. Bulbs placed diagonally adjacent to a numbered cell do not contribute to the bulb count. An unnumbered black cell may have any number of light bulbs adjacent to it, or none at all, and not all light bulbs are necessarily clued via black squares.

0				1		1			0
				1				2	
		0					2		1
1			■	1	0				
		1	1			1	2		
			■						
						0			0
	0	1			0				

The numbers 1 to 9 must be placed into the individual cells of each of the six large triangles.

No digit appears more than once in any horizontal row or diagonal line of any length, even those rows and lines interrupted by the central hexagon.

Some numbers are already in place.

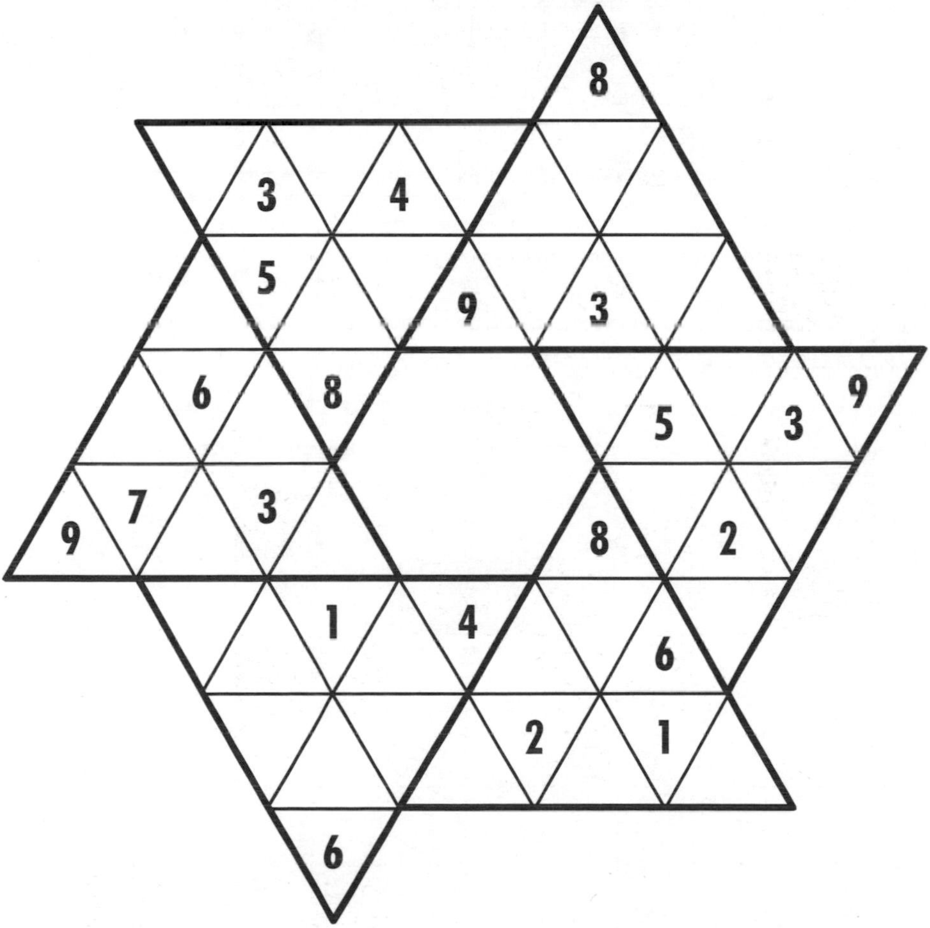

8

3 4

5 9 3

6 8 5 3 9

9 7 3 8 2

1 4 6

2 1

6

What letter should replace the question mark?

E	F	P
M	H	F
V	B	C
G	E	O
S	C	E
F	?	G

When the box below is folded to form a cube, just one of the five options (A, B, C, D or E) can NOT be produced. Which?

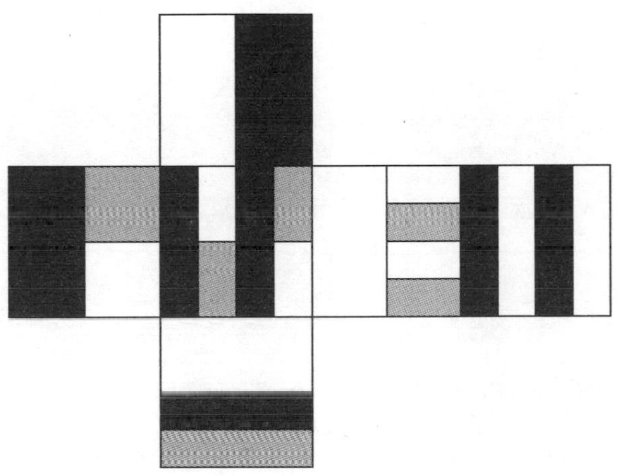

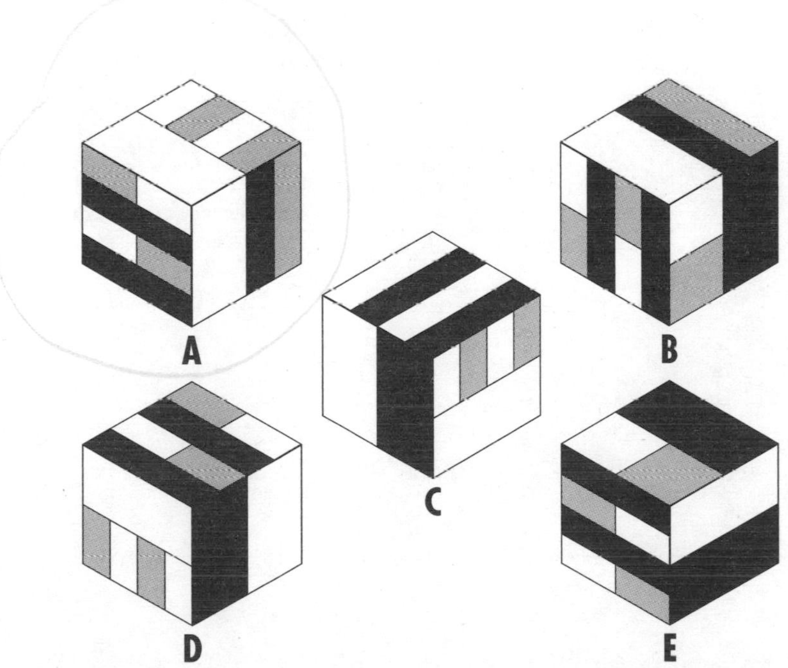

What number should replace the question mark?

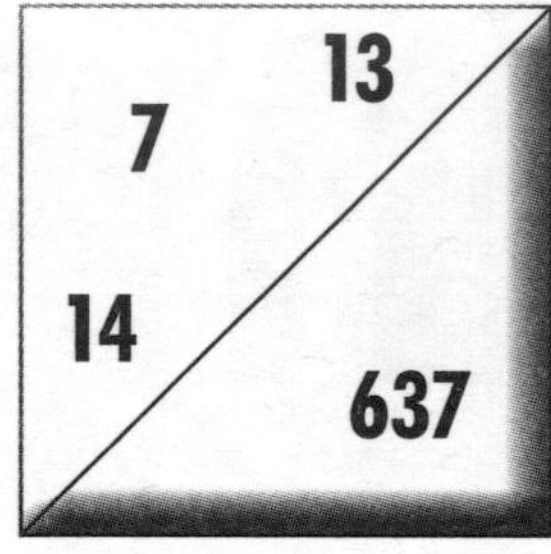

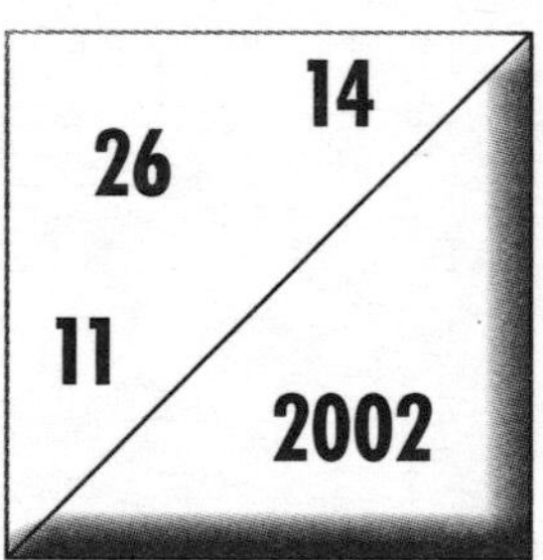

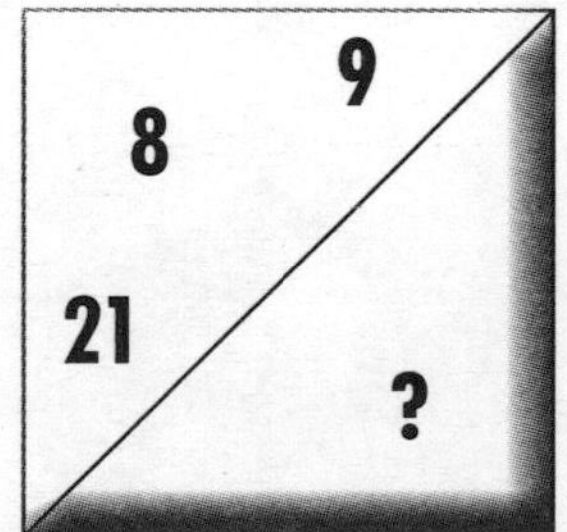

23

Daisy the cat rolls a 30 mm diameter ball exactly three times around the perimeter of a room measuring five metres by four metres.

How many revolutions will the ball make, to the nearest whole number?

> ***'I believe that at the end of the century ... one will be able to speak of machines thinking without expecting to be contradicted.'***

What letter should replace the question mark?

B	T
N	

K	W
S	

P	Y
V	

X	?
N	

What numbers should replace the question marks?

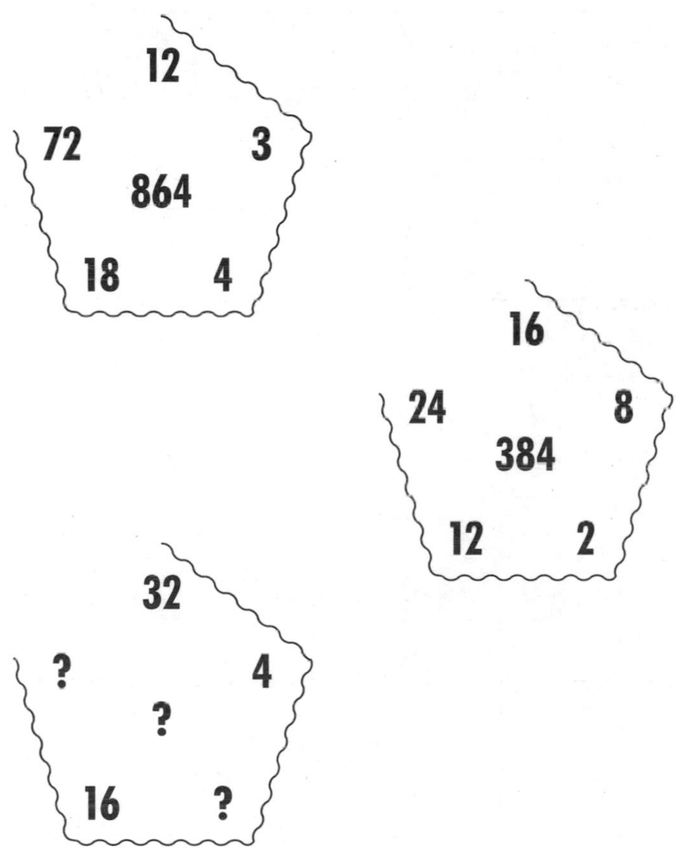

Place either X or 0 into each empty square, so that no four consecutive squares in a straight line in any direction (horizontally, vertically, or diagonally) contain more than three of the same symbol.

	X	X	X				X	X
		X	O	X	X	O		
	X						O	
		O		O	X		O	X
X		X	X					X
O	X				O		X	
	X		O	X			O	
		X				O	O	X
		O						
	O	O	O	X	O		O	
		O	O			O	X	
X		X					O	X
X	O			O		O		
							O	
X				X		X	X	
O		X		X		O		
X	X	O	O			X	X	

Which of the alternatives (A, B, C, or D) should replace the question mark?

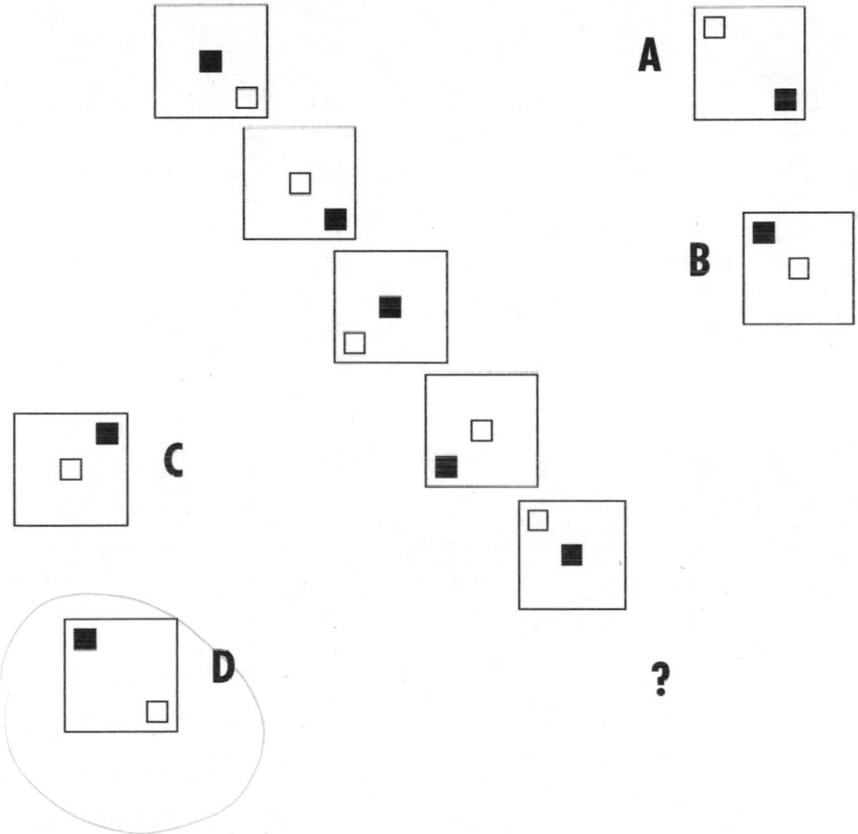

A

B

C

D

?

What number should replace the question mark?

3	26
7	546

4	37
8	1184

5	35
6	1050

2	23
9	?

What number should replace the question mark?

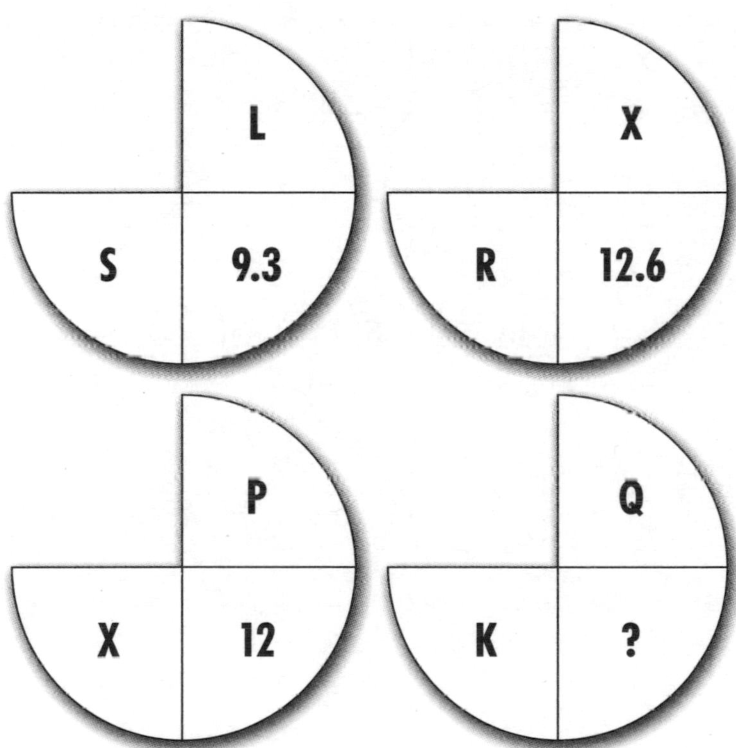

Fill each empty circle with one of the numbers 1-7. Every horizontal row, vertical column, set of seven linked circles, and diagonal line of seven circles should contain seven different numbers.

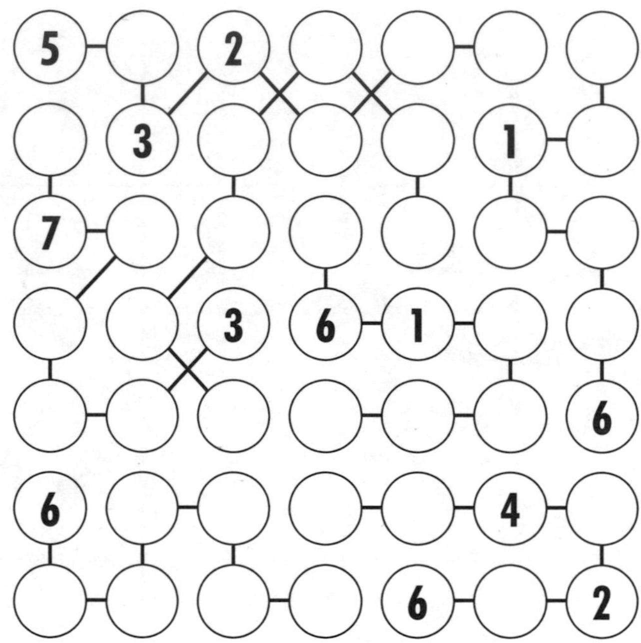

What number should replace the question mark?

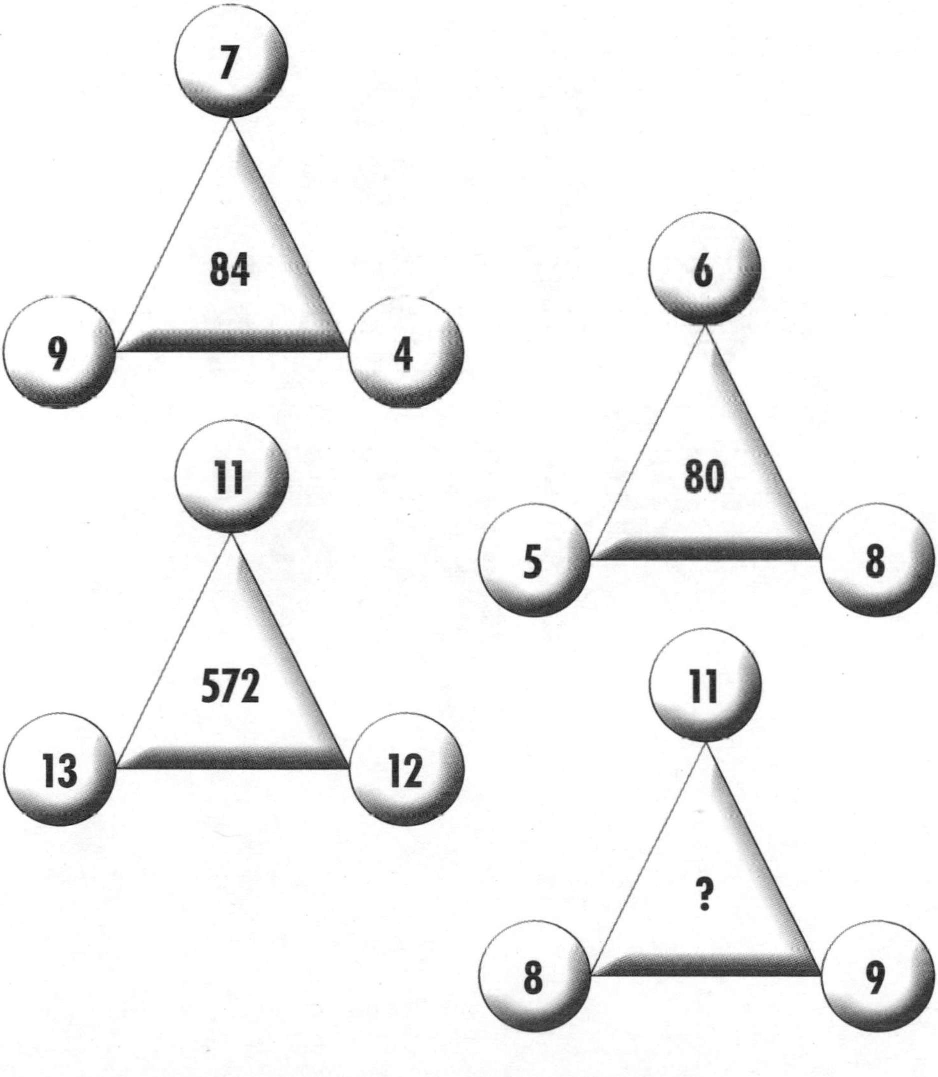

7

84

9 4

6

80

5 8

11

572

13 12

11

?

8 9

What letters should replace the question marks?

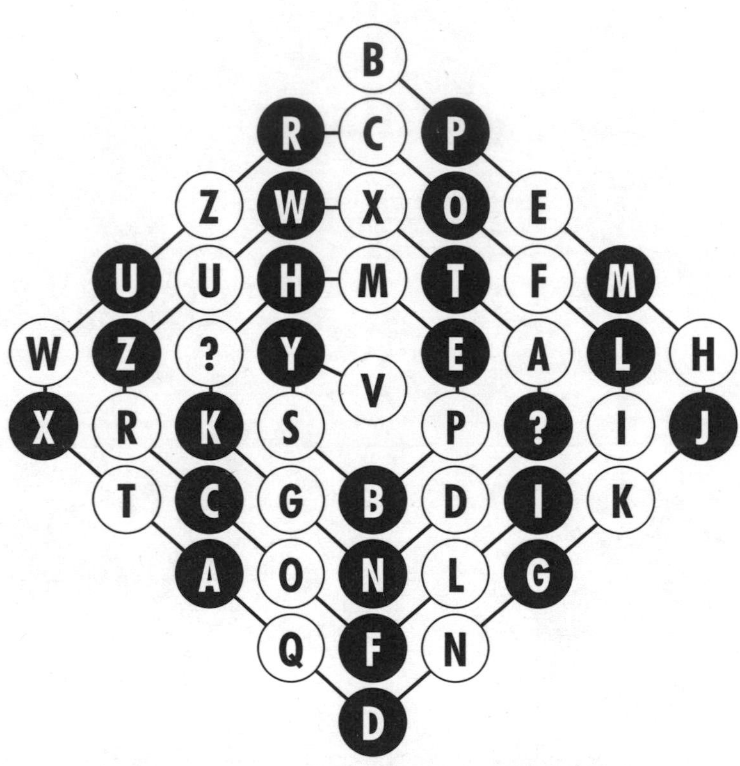

What number should replace the question mark?

REMBRANDT = 16

TINTORETTO = 16

BOTTICELLI = 14

VERMEER = 18

DONATELLO = ?

Turing is considered the 'father of modern computing'. He gave the earliest known lecture to mention computer intelligence in 1947.

What number should replace the question mark?

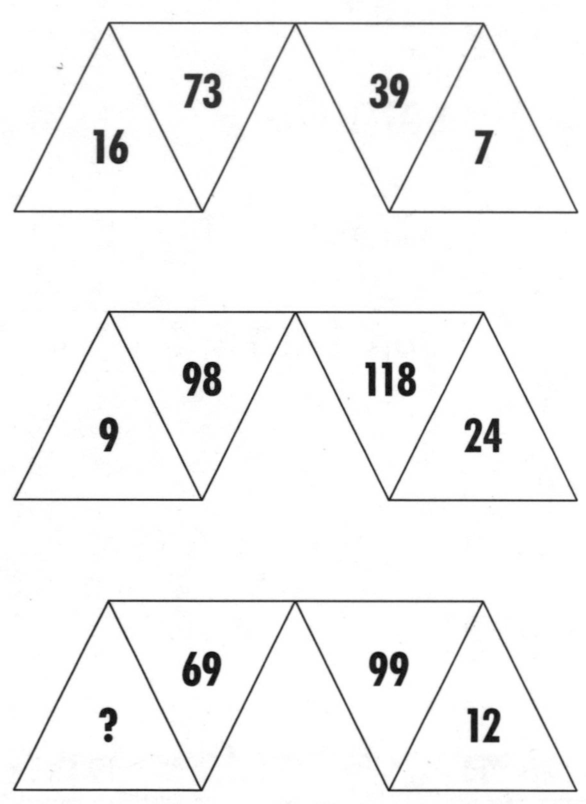

Which of the alternatives (A, B, C, D, or E) should replace the question mark?

-1	6	0
2	4	3
2	7	-2

6	5	1
11	7	8
2	6	2

6	14	8
10	10	7
6	11	3

10	13	8
15	13	16
7	10	10

?

A

11	18	15
14	17	12
14	19	10

B

10	19	14
15	16	14
12	18	11

C

14	14	11
19	16	18
10	15	12

D

11	18	12
14	17	15
14	19	10

E

11	18	12
14	16	15
14	19	10

Place the numbers 1 to 6 into each row and column, one number per square. Each number represents a skyscraper of that many floors.

Arrange the skyscrapers in such a way that the given number outside the grid represents the number of buildings which can be seen from that point, looking only at that number's row or column.

A skyscraper with a lower number of floors cannot hide a higher building, but one with a higher number of floors always hides any lower building behind it.

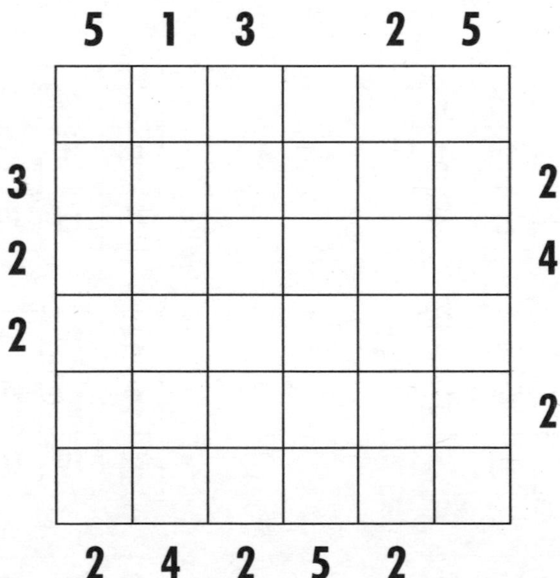

What number should replace the question mark?

389	123
43	12

245	777
19	54

357	241
7	86

?	876
131	13

What numbers should replace the question marks?

47	16	63	31
31	13	18	18
54	28	26	26
16	45	61	29
25	61	86	36
47	?	39	?

Given that scales A and B balance perfectly, how many hearts are needed to balance scale C?

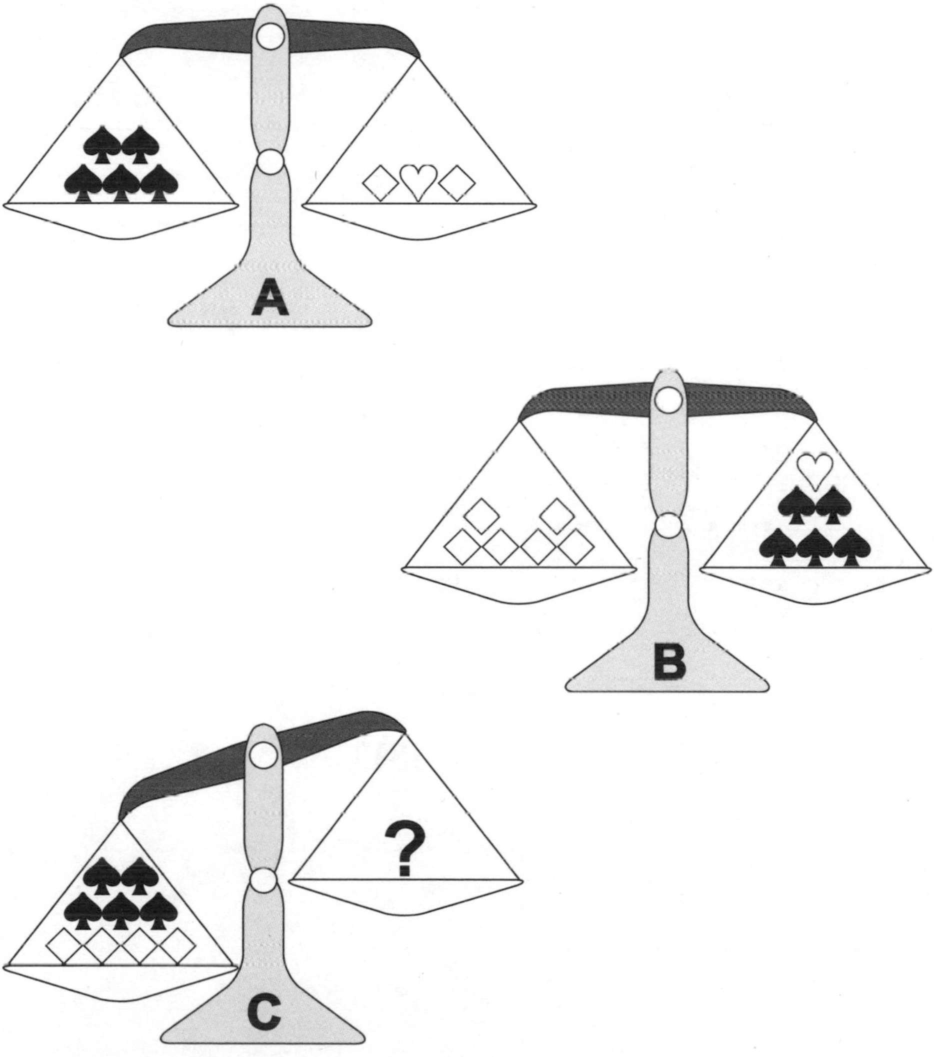

What number should replace the question mark?

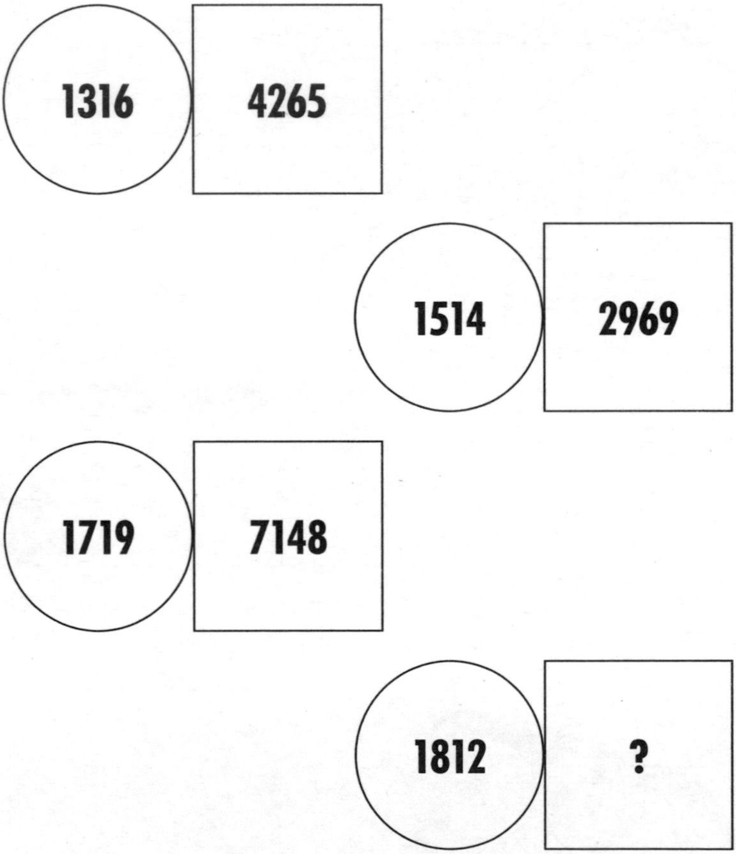

Circle	Square
1316	4265
1514	2969
1719	7148
1812	?

What number should replace the question mark?

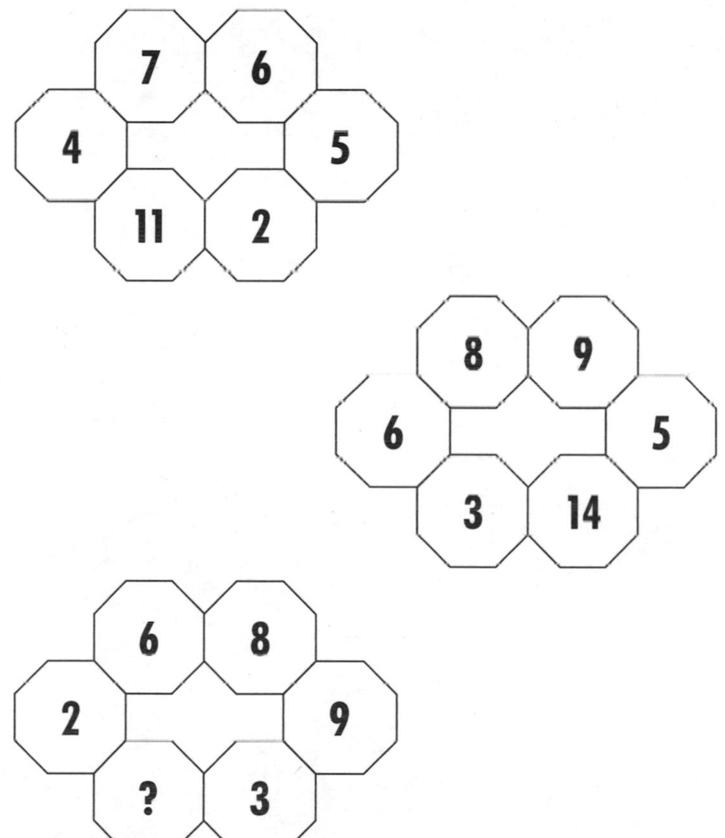

When the box below is folded to form a cube, just one of the five options (A, B, C, D or E) can be produced. Which?

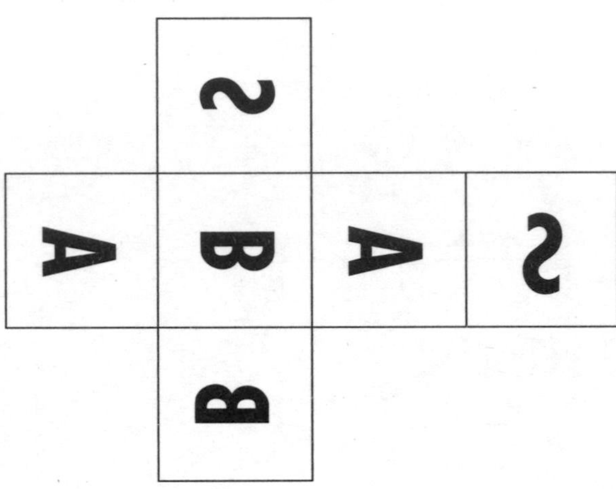

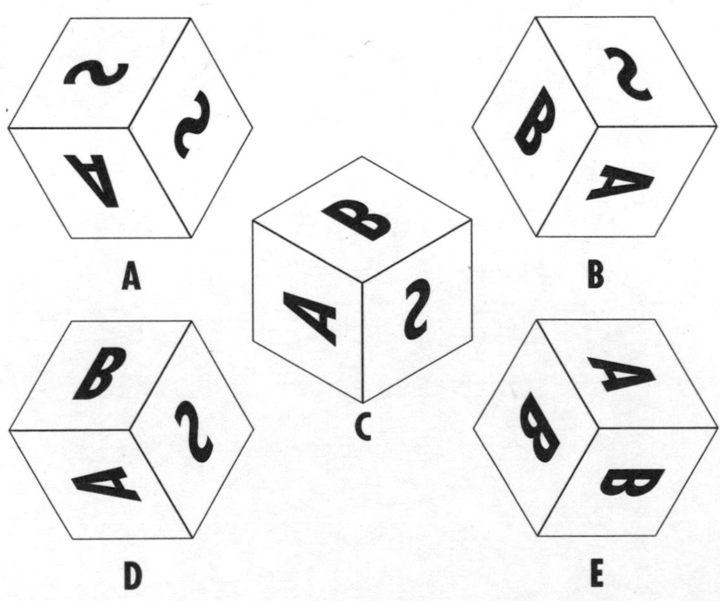

A fish pond with a capacity of 5,000 litres needs its water to be recirculated every 45 minutes, and Bill needs to choose a pump capable of achieving this.

Pump A works at a rate of 6,000 litres per hour, pump B works at a rate of 6,500 litres per hour, and pump C works at a rate of 6,750 litres per hour.

Which pump should Bill choose as a minimum requirement for his needs?

He has as good brains as any boy that's been here, & they are good enough for him to get through even in 'useless' subjects like Latin & French & English.

From Alan Turing's school report, Lent Term 1928

What numbers should replace the question marks?

What numbers and letters should replace the question marks?

5	21	10	?	15	16	23	12
F	N	V	?	L	O	Q	K
18	13	25	?	5	9	1	15
R	T	Z	?	B	N	V	I
26	23	19	?	22	4	13	20
H	W	G	?	N	B	D	E
20	11	15	?	8	13	21	7
M	T	F	?	G	S	N	L

What number should replace the question mark?

In terms of area, what is the answer, to the nearest square millimetre?

(A – B) + C

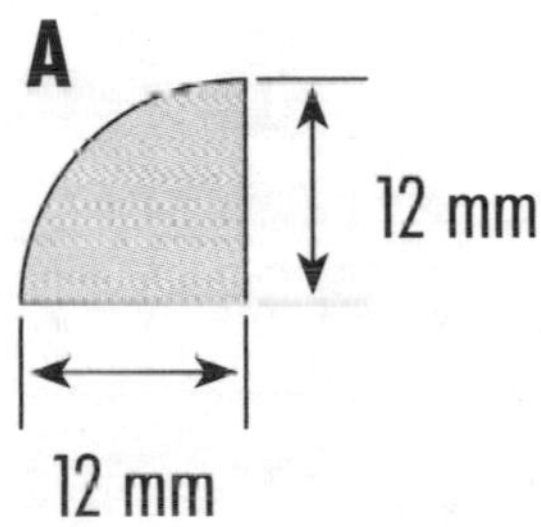

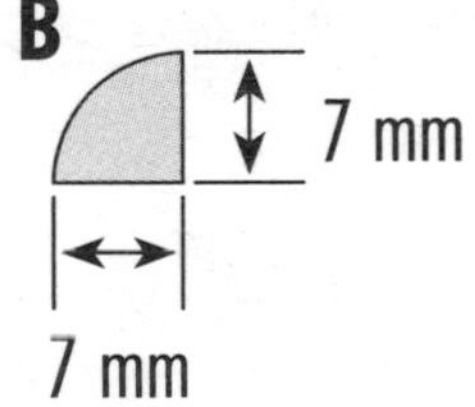

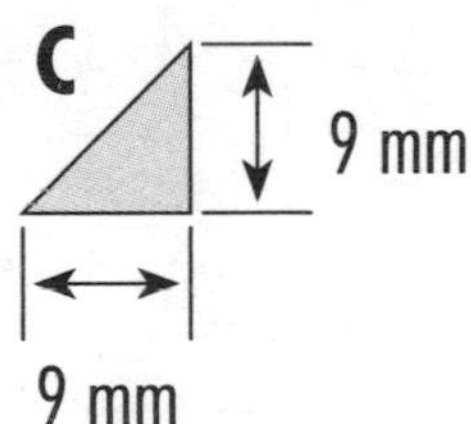

What number should replace the question mark?

3	21	15	11	9
27	6	23	3	16
14	31	33	18	19
6	17	26	9	22
29	4	11	28	3
14	12	24	10	7
5	13	8	31	?

What number should replace the question mark?

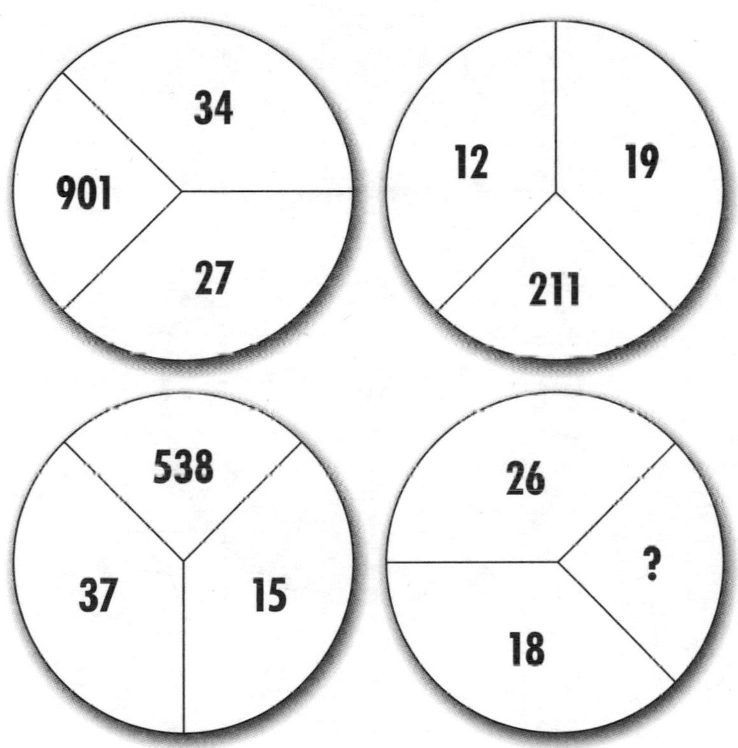

Two of the clocks below are faulty. Both were set to the correct time at midday (12 o'clock) today, as was the largest clock, which works normally, keeping perfect time.

The hands on clock A move anticlockwise (counterclockwise), at twice the normal speed of time. The hands on clock B move clockwise, at one third the normal speed of time. It is now 9:30 in the evening, and therefore nine and a half hours have passed since midday.

Draw in the hands on both faulty clocks, to illustrate the time each is now showing.

12 1 2 3 4 5 6 7 8 9 10 11

Clock A

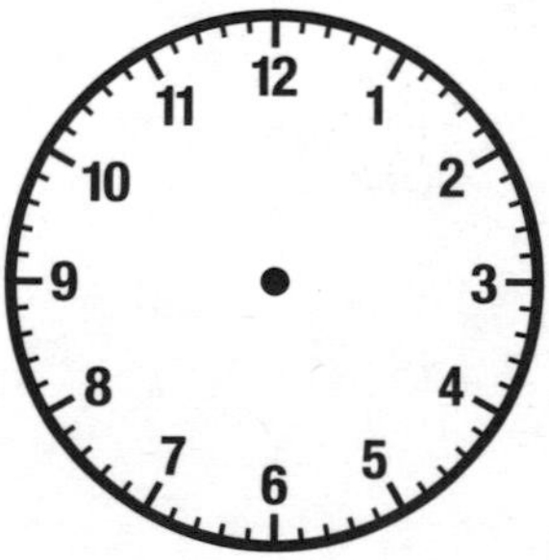

12 1 2 3 4 5 6 7 8 9 10 11

Clock B

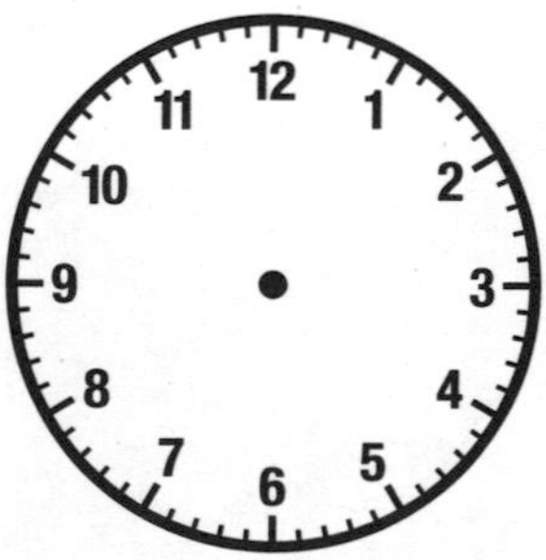

12 1 2 3 4 5 6 7 8 9 10 11

What percentage of the circles below are white?

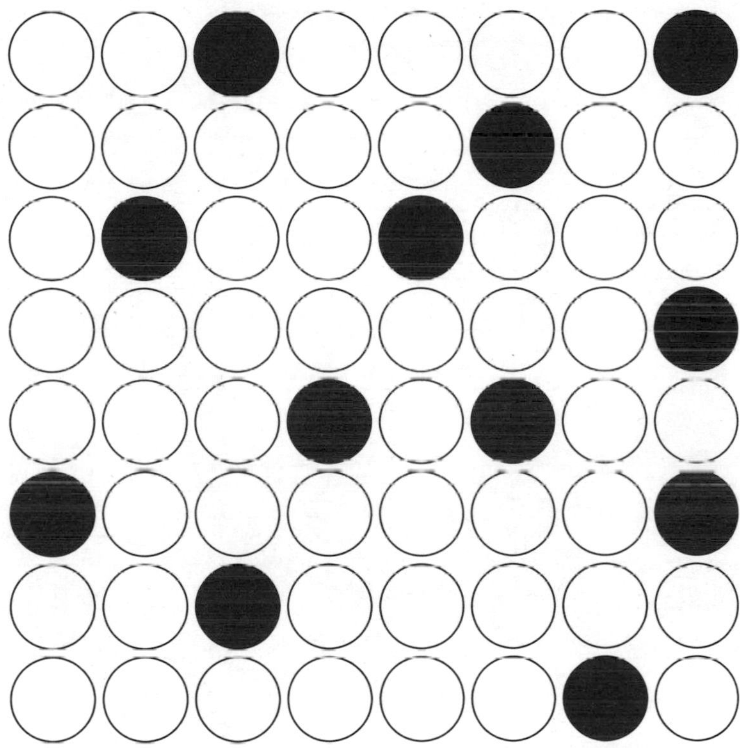

What letter should replace the question mark?

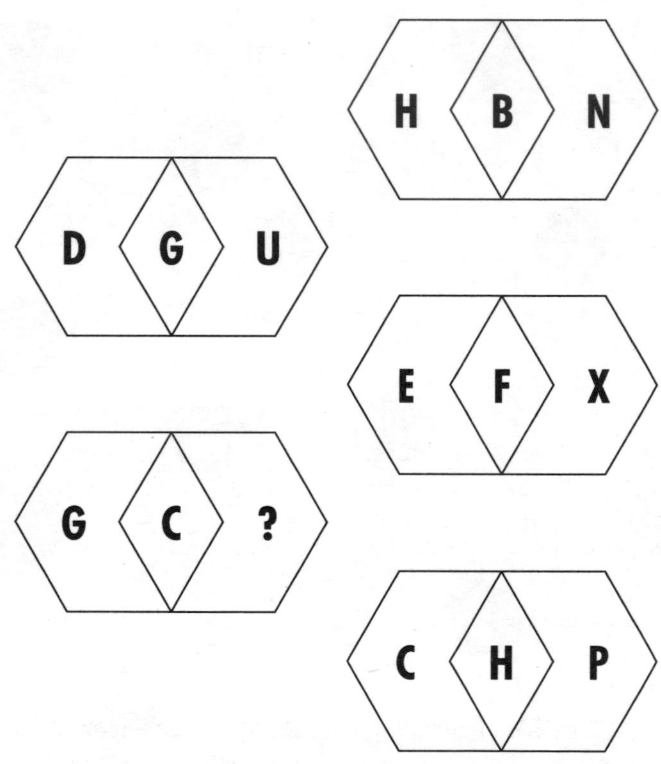

A sign box with dimensions of 4.1 metres long, 0.3 metres high, and 0.14 metres deep is made from steel and perspex; steel forming the back, top, bottom, and two ends, and perspex forming the front panel.

Steel weighs 4.6 kilograms per square metre, and perspex weighs 5.3 kilograms per square metre.

What is the total weight of the sign box?

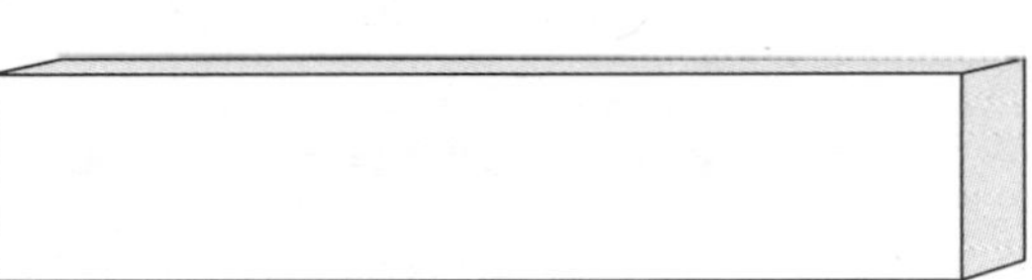

Turing's article 'Computing machinery and intelligence' led to what is now known as the Turing Test, which gauges a machine's ability to demonstrate intelligent behaviour equivalent to or indistinguishable from a human.

Four bricks are on a revolving plate, and can be drawn from different angles in two dimensions, so that faces from three bricks can be seen, and the face of the fourth brick is hidden from view by one of those three bricks.

Which of the diagrams shown below are correct, given that they may be rotated?

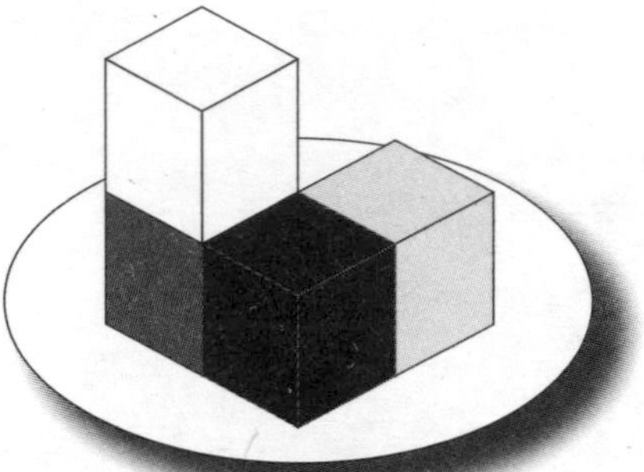

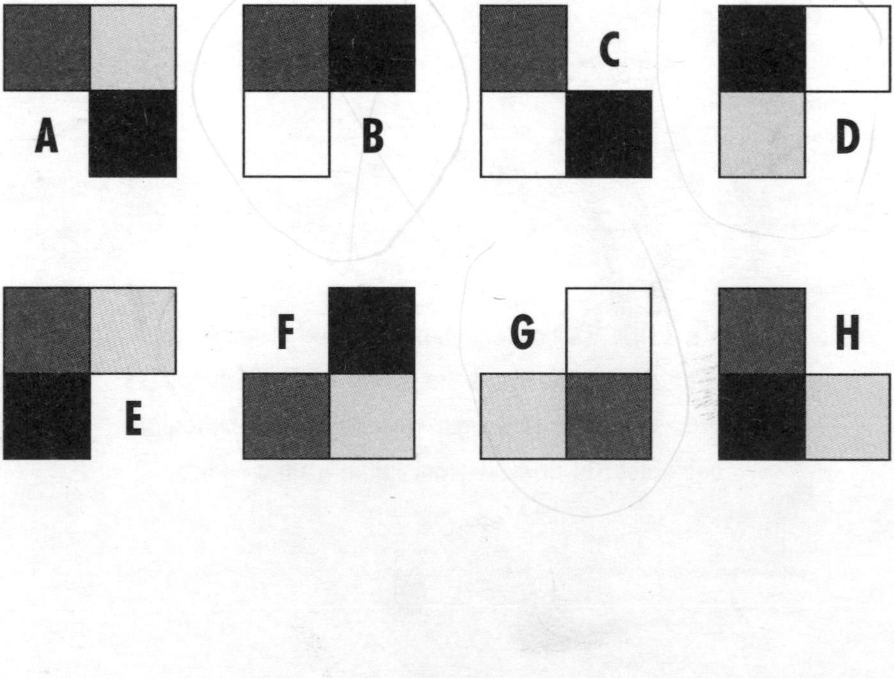

A

B

C

D

E

F

G

H

What numbers should replace the question marks?

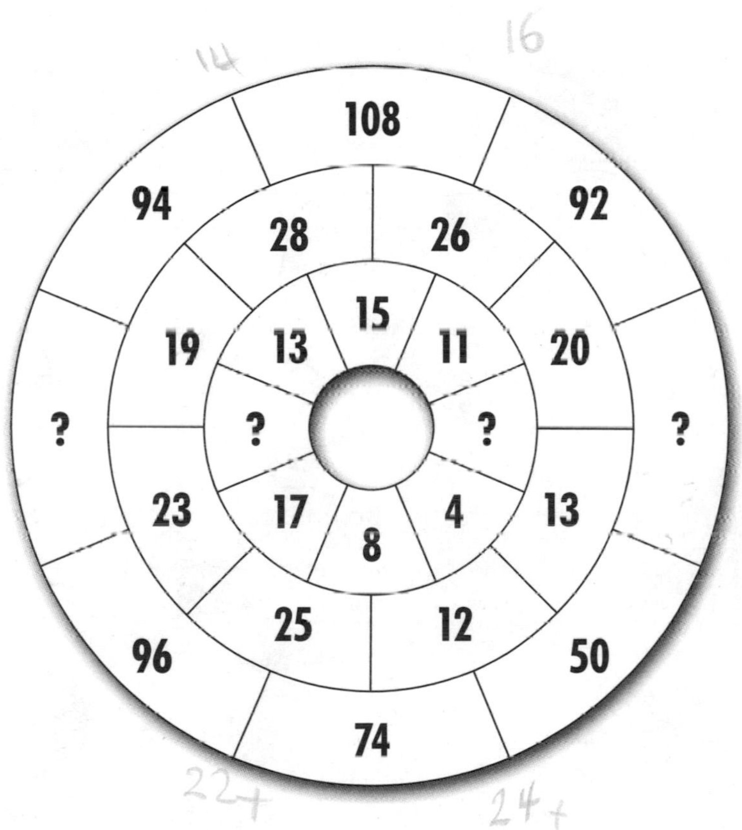

Which of the alternatives (A, B, C, or D) should replace the question mark?

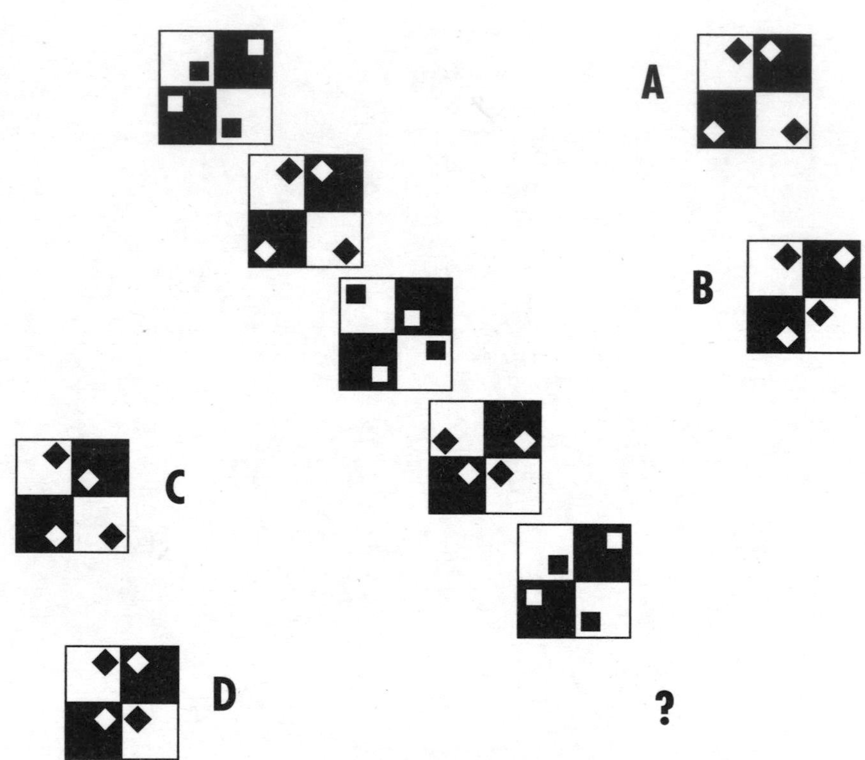

What numbers should replace the question marks?

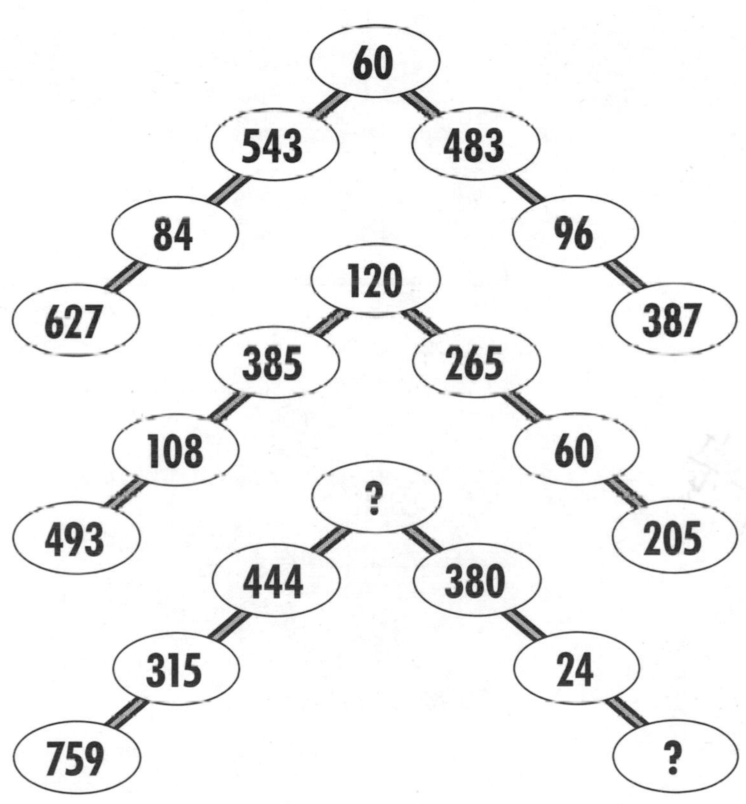

What number should replace the question mark?

12

36

324

2916

52488

?

What numbers should replace the question marks?

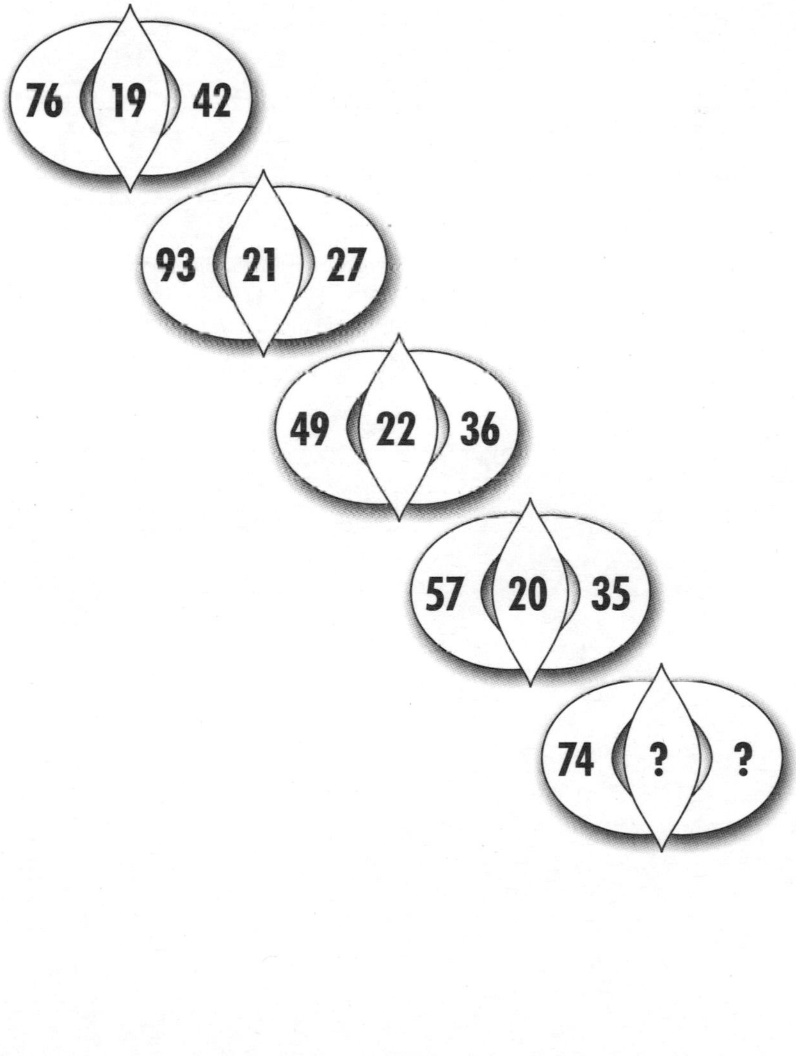

76	19	42
93	21	27
49	22	36
57	20	35
74	?	?

What number should replace the question mark?

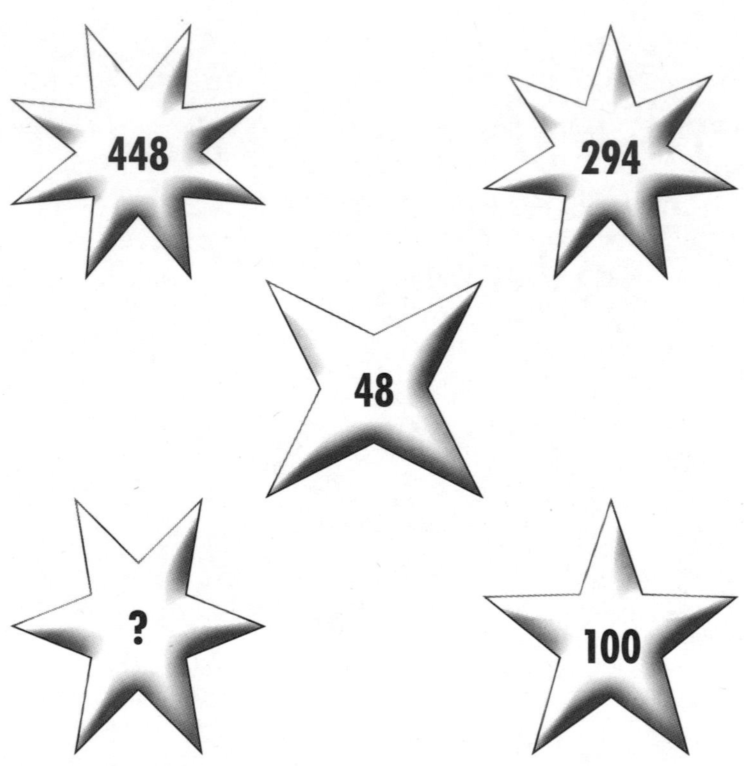

What letter should replace the question mark?

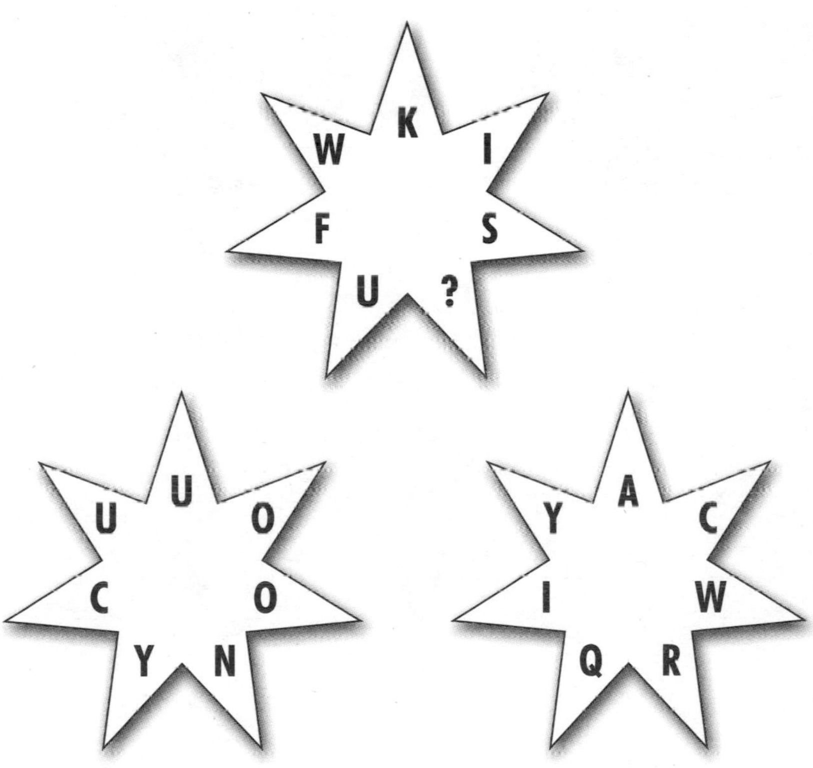

Which of the alternatives (A, B, C, D, or E) should replace the question mark?

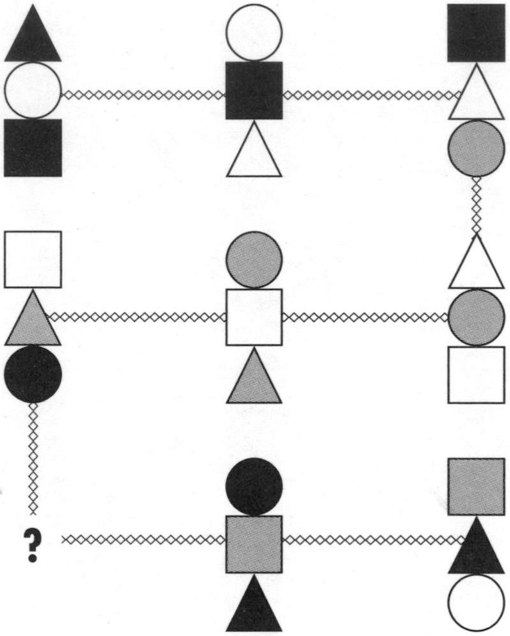

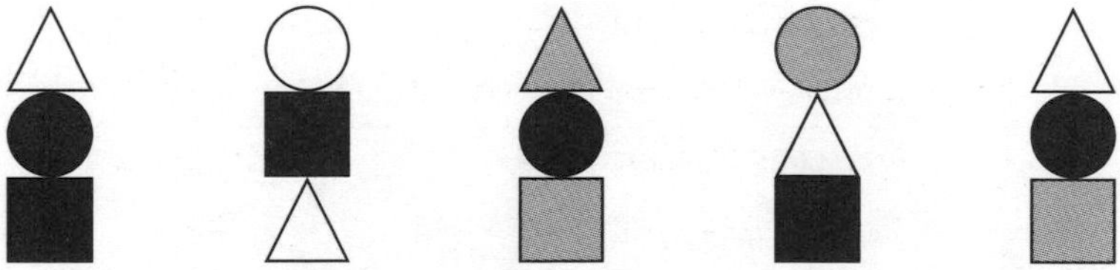

?

A B C D E

Peter is about to buy his first car. His father has told him that he will pay 40% of the total price of the car, plus 100% of all taxes relating to the purchase.

The car is for sale at $14,000, plus taxes of 18%.

What is the total price of the car plus taxes, and how much will Peter's father give him towards the purchase?

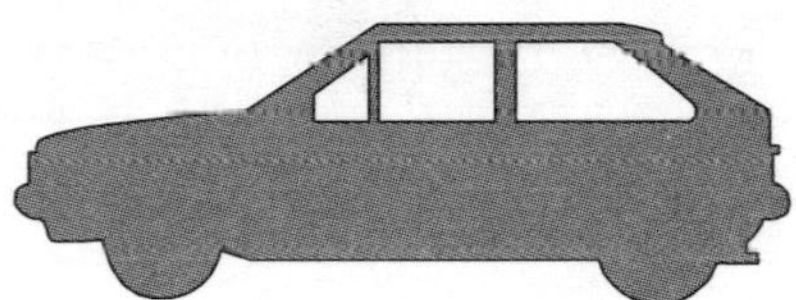

During World War II Turing was the main man responsible for breaking the Enigma code used by the Germans at Bletchley Park, the wartime station of the Government Code and Cypher School.

The steel bars below are not drawn to scale, although the dimensions given are correct. Which steel bar is the heaviest?

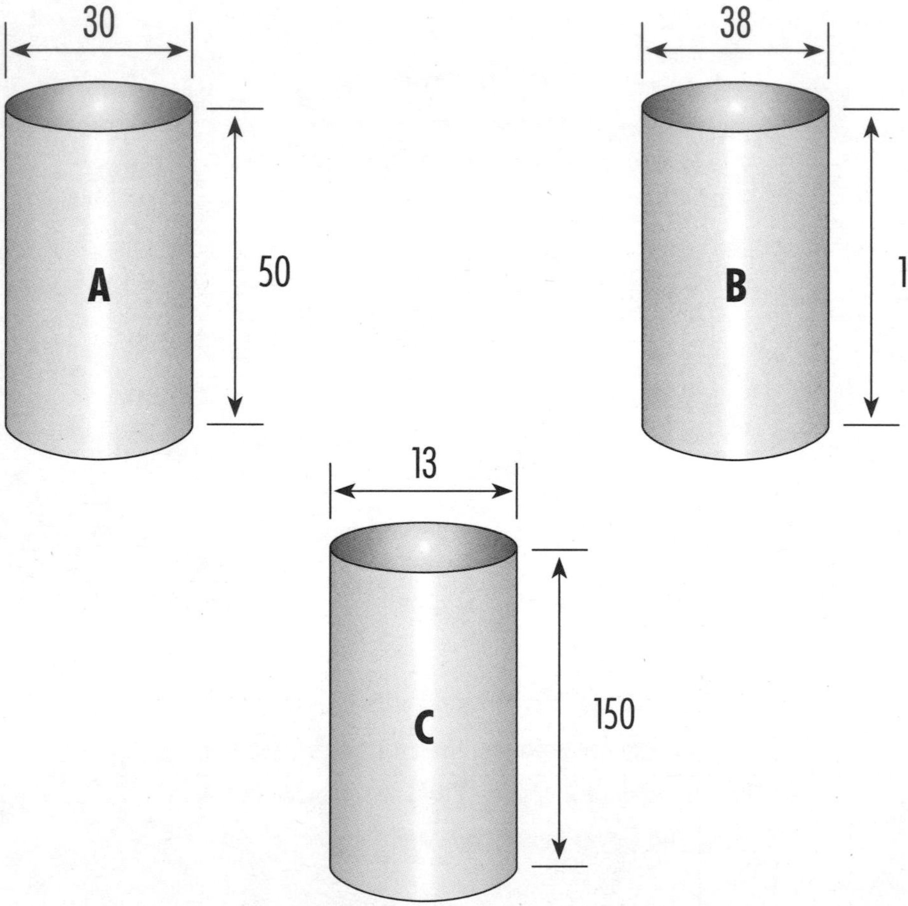

A: 30 (diameter), 50 (height)

B: 38 (diameter), 19 (height)

C: 13 (diameter), 150 (height)

Place circles (representing light bulbs) in some of the empty squares, in such a way that no two bulbs shine on each other, until every square of the grid is lit up. A bulb sends rays of light horizontally and vertically, illuminating its entire row and column unless its light is blocked by a black cell.

Some black cells contain numbers, indicating how many light bulbs are in adjacent squares either immediately above, below, to the right or to the left. Bulbs placed diagonally adjacent to a numbered cell do not contribute to the bulb count. An unnumbered black cell may have any number of light bulbs adjacent to it, or none at all, and not all light bulbs are necessarily clued via black squares.

		■ 2		■ 1	■ 1			■	
					■ 0	■ 2			
	■ 1		■	■ 0					
			■ 1				■		
■ 0				■ 2				■ 3	
	■ 1		■ 2						
							■ 1		
			■ 0			■ 1	■ 2		
	■ 2		■ 0						■

What letter should replace the question mark?

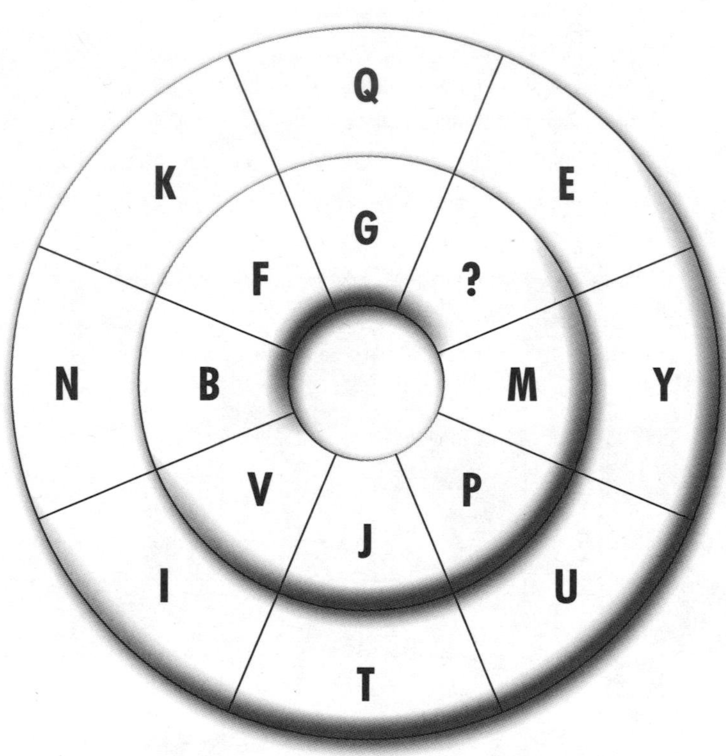

Fill each empty circle with one of the numbers 1-8. Each horizontal row, vertical column, set of eight linked circles, and diagonal line of eight circles should contain eight different numbers.

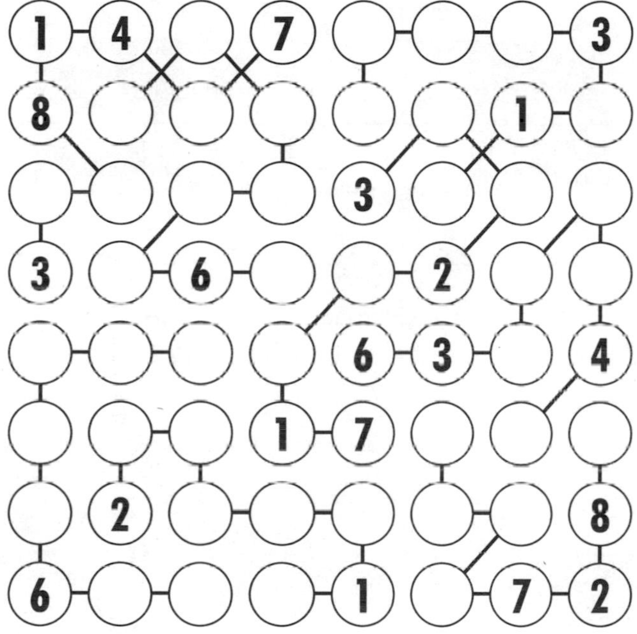

When the box below is folded to form a cube, just one of the five options (A, B, C, D or E) can NOT be produced. Which?

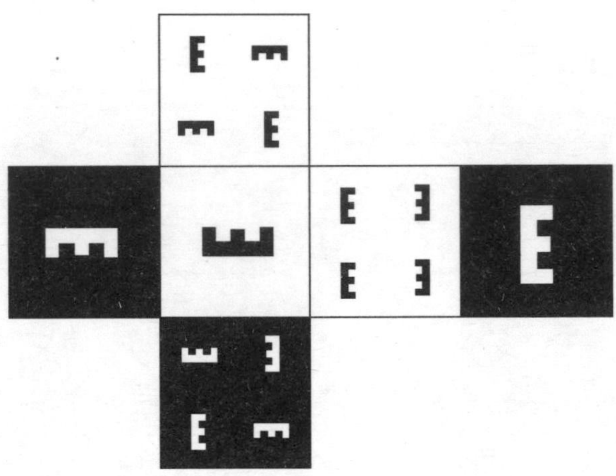

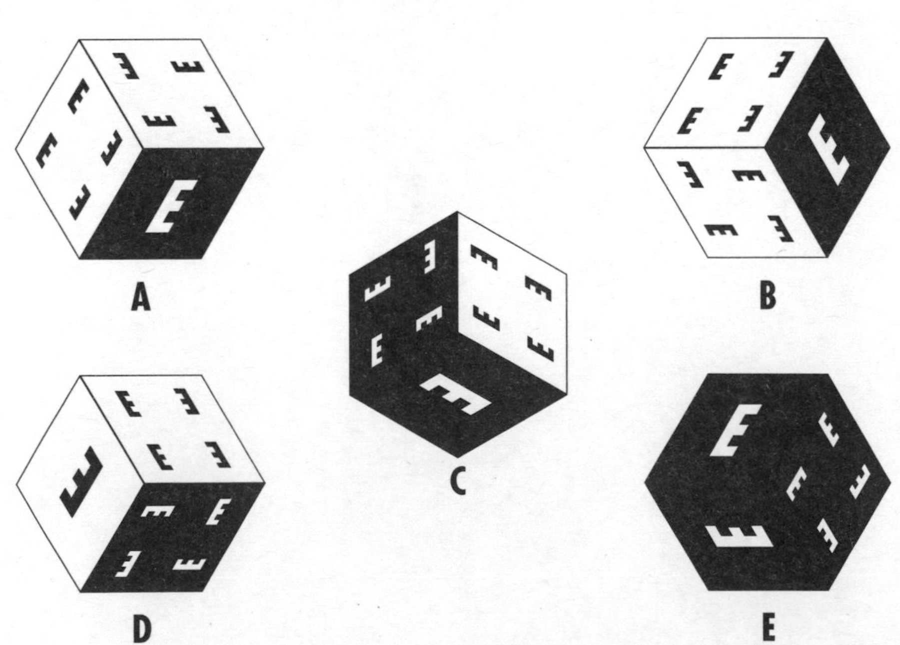

What number should replace the question mark?

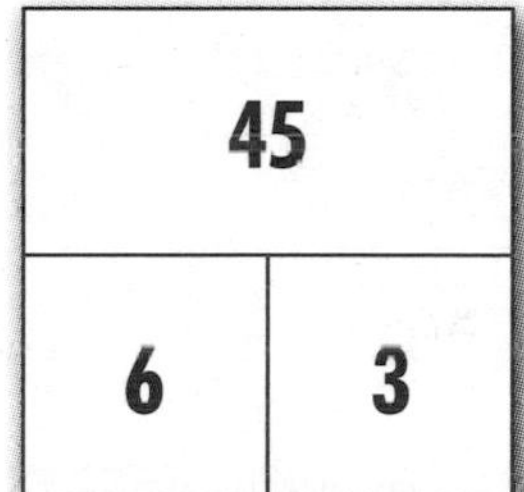

89	
5	8

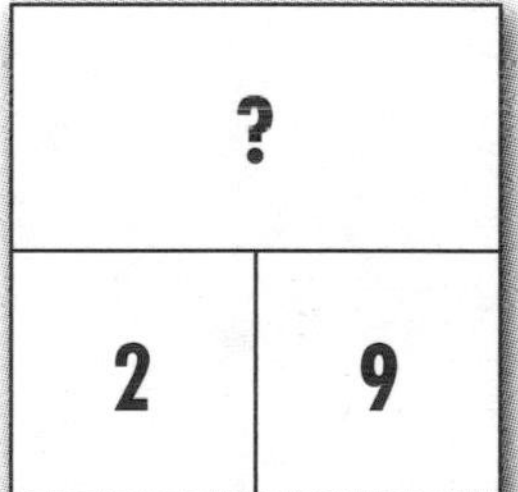

What letter should replace the question mark?

B	D	F	C
H	I	G	K
F	I	I	J
J	N	L	Q
L	S	Q	?

What number should replace the question mark?

56	72	7
	8	63
	91	9
13	104	?

What number should replace the question mark?

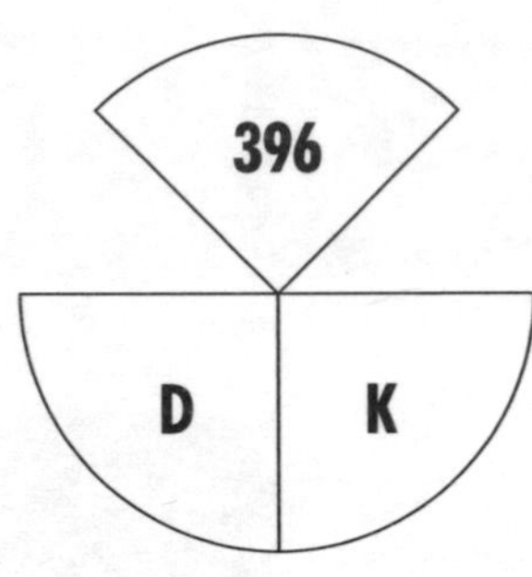

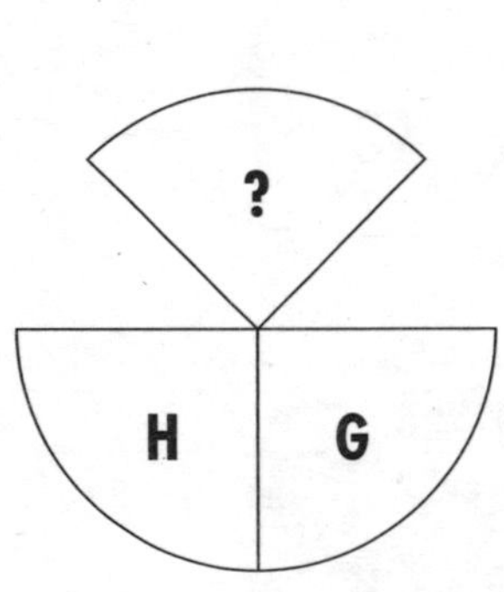

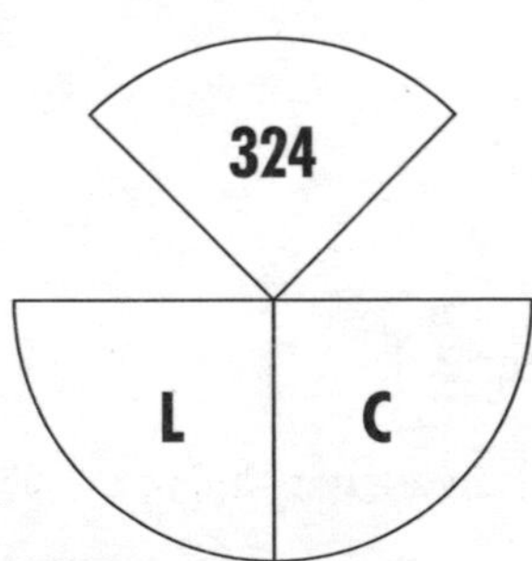

Simon bought two kilos of fish and three kilos of potatoes today.

Sarah bought one kilo of fish and one kilo of potatoes today, paying a total price of $4.20.

Given that one kilo of fish costs $2.30 more than one kilo of potatoes, what was Simon's bill?

As well as being an incredible intellect, Alan Turing was a well-regarded athlete, and came fifth in a qualifying marathon for the 1948 Olympics.

What letter and what number should replace the question marks?

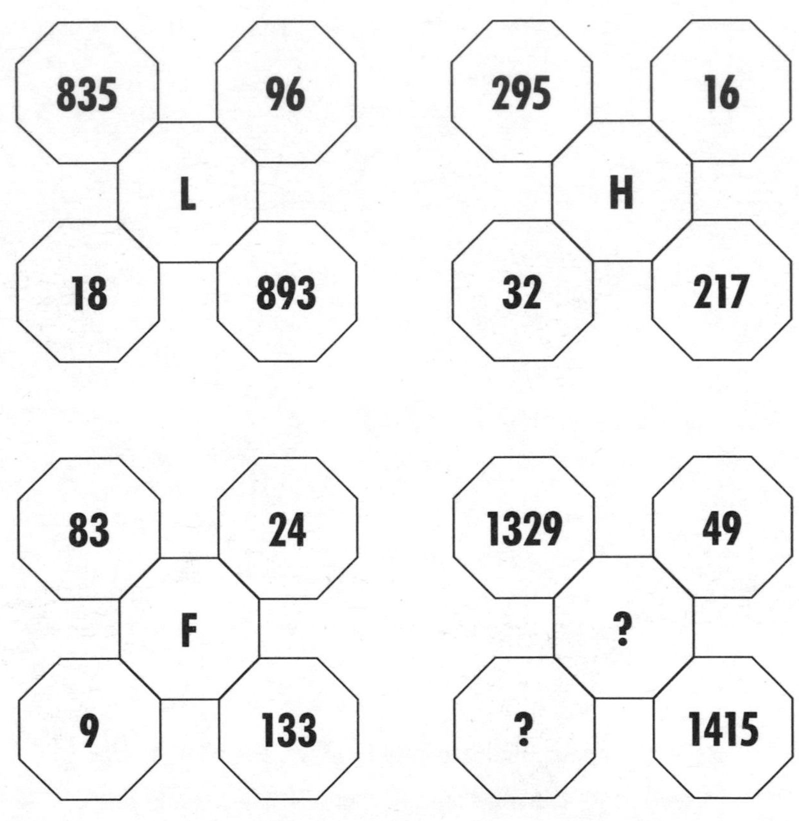

What number should replace the question mark?

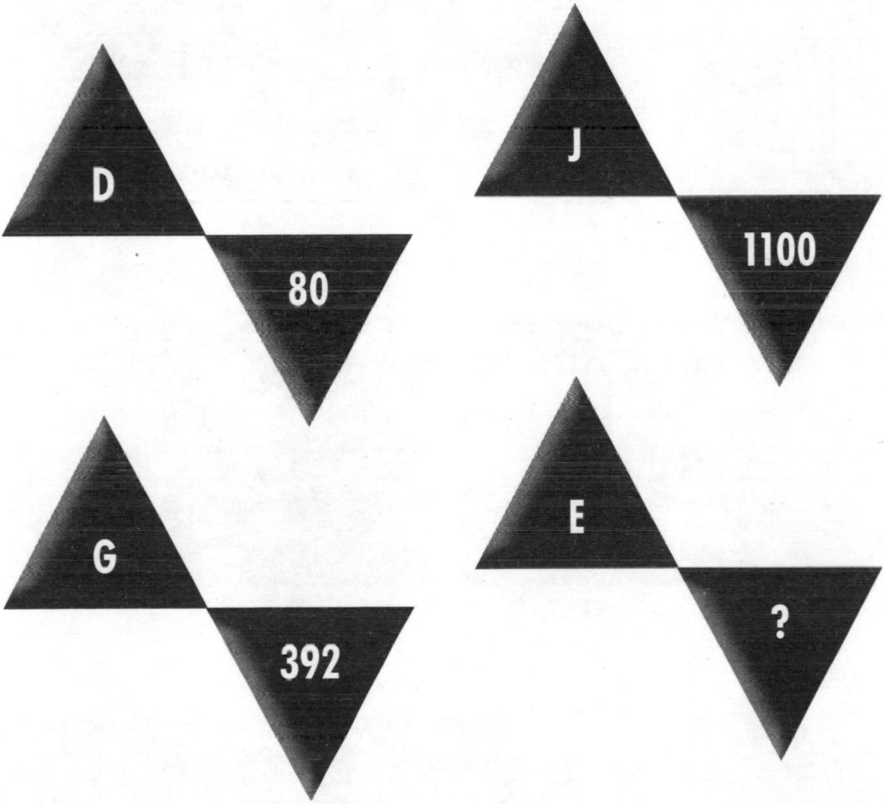

D
80

J
1100

G
392

E
?

In design H, which numbered square(s) should be shaded black in order to continue the pattern shown in the sequence A, B, C, D, E, F, and G?

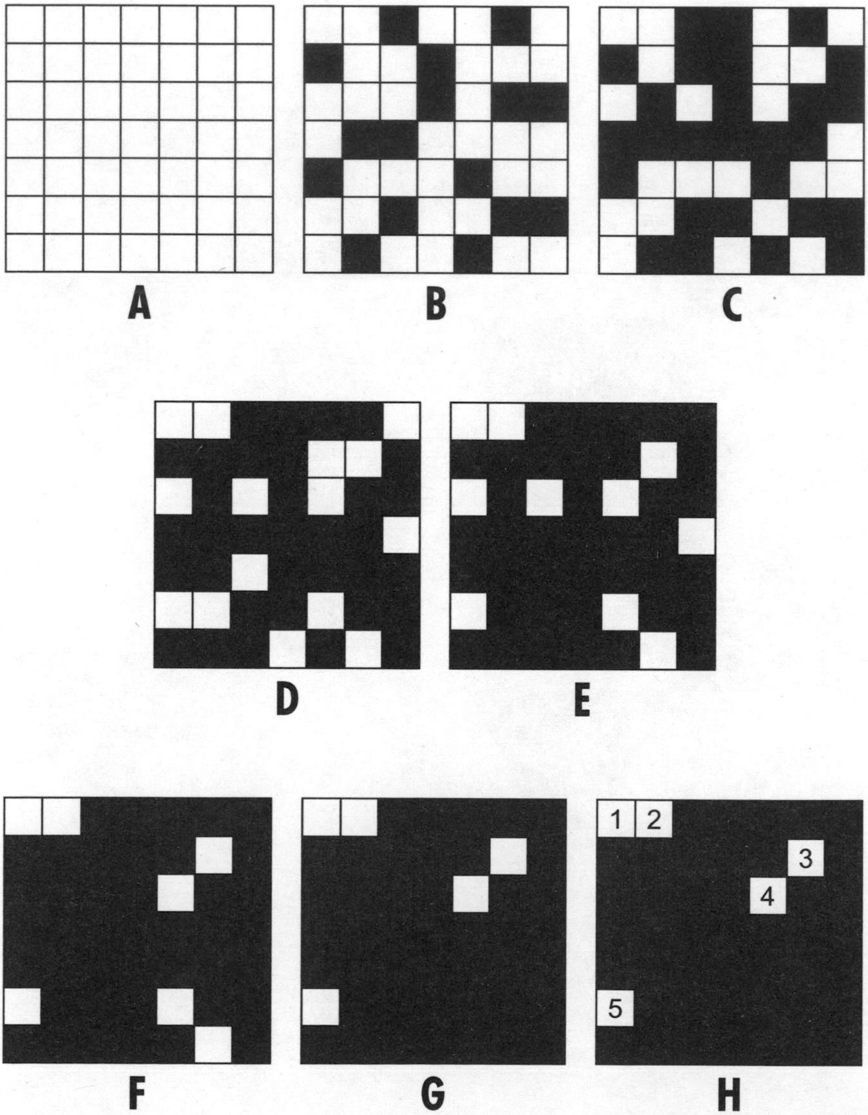

A

B

C

D

E

F

G

1 2
3
4
5

H

What letter should replace the question mark?

R
S K
A X
V L
T

T
E H
? R
K W
S

H
M Q
D U
Z Y
I

O
M Q
L B
Y X
K

L
N J
O Y
B C
P

I
H P
Z C
E O
G

G
V S
T I
P D
H

S
N J
W F
A B
R

Which of the alternatives (A, B, C, or D) should replace the question mark?

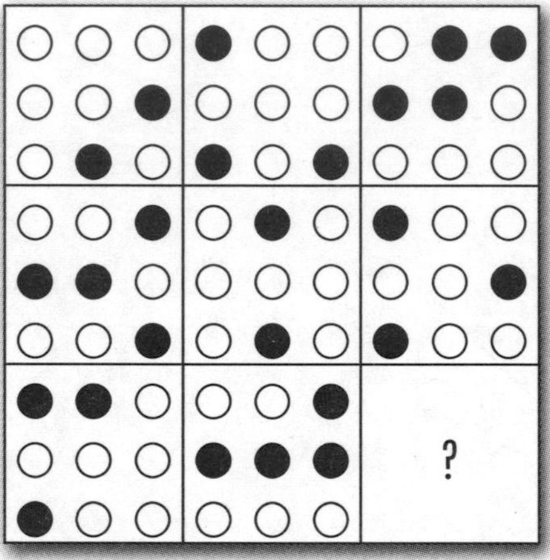

A

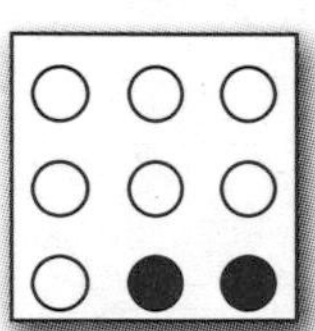

B

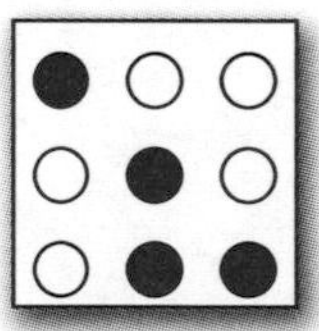

C

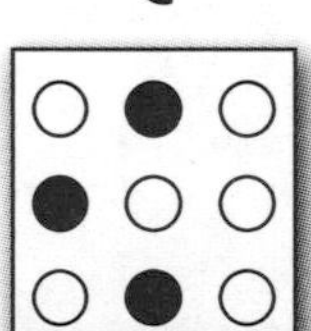

D

What number should replace the question mark?

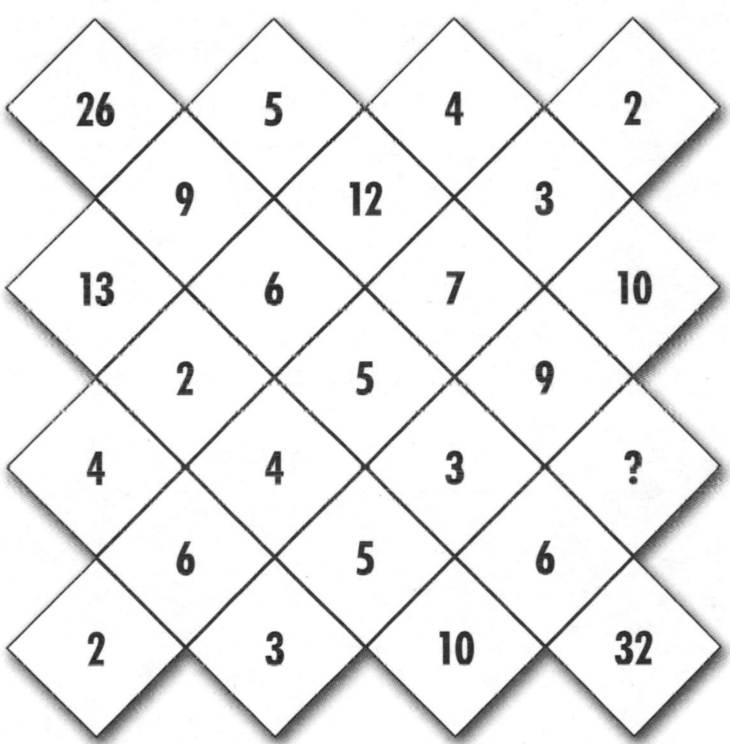

Which of the alternatives (A, B, C, D, or E)
should replace the question mark?

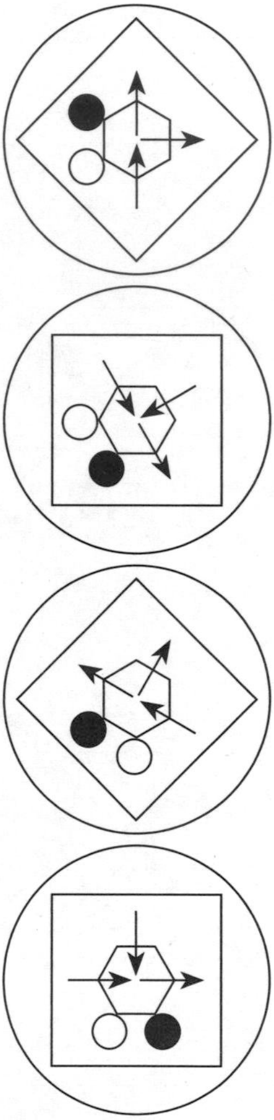

?

A

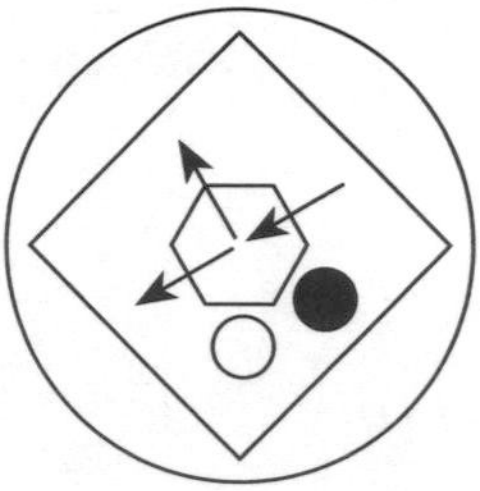

B

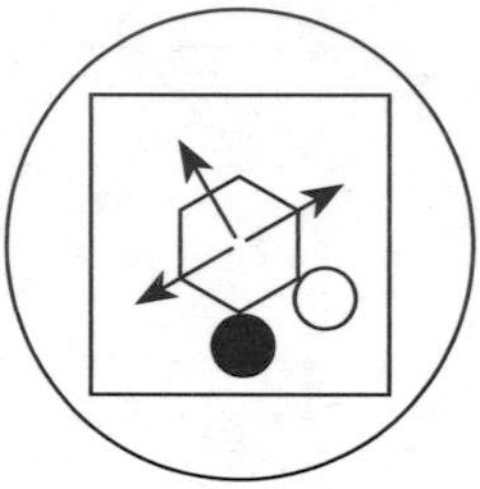

C

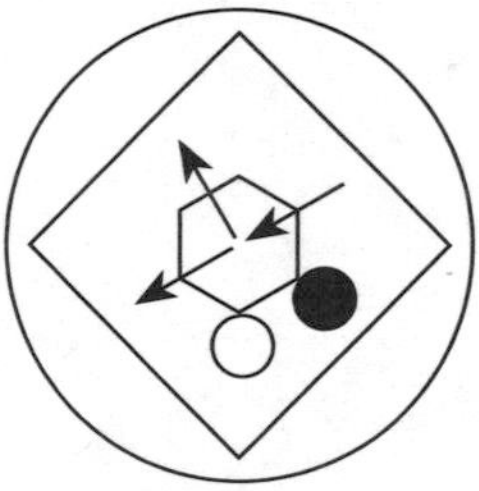

D

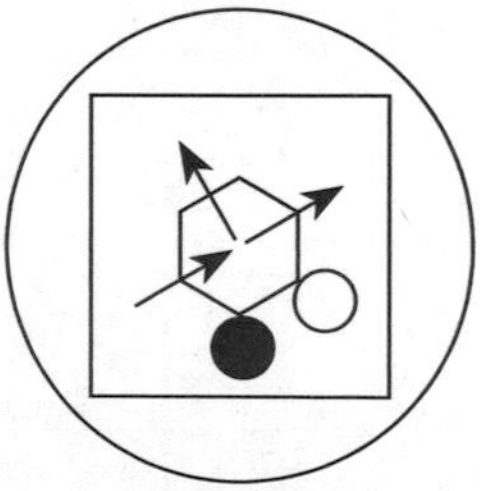

E

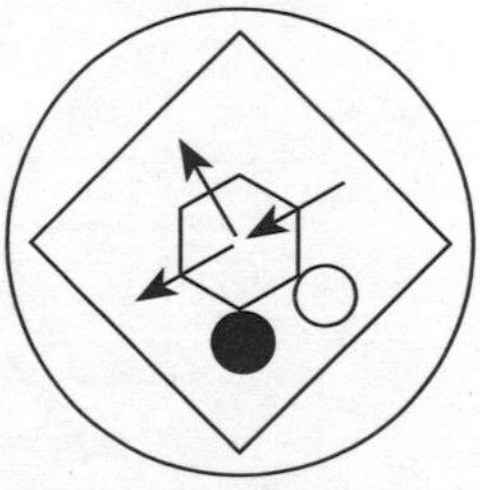

Which strip belongs to row D?

A		★		★		▲		■
B	▲	▲		■			★	
C		■		■		★		▲
D								
E				▲	▲	■		★
F	■	■		★			▲	
G					★	★	▲	■
H		▲			▲		■	★

1	■			■			★	▲
2	★			▲		■		★
3		▲		▲			■	★
4	★				★	▲	■	

Which of the alternatives (A, B, C, D, or E) should replace the question mark?

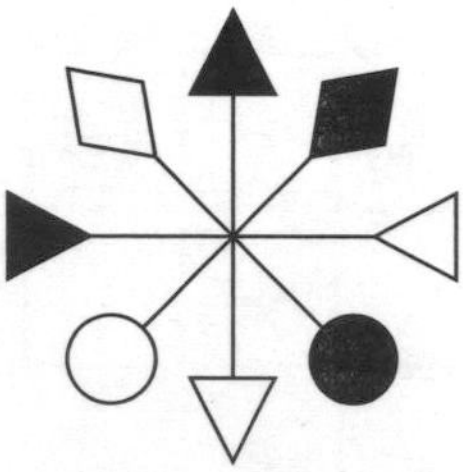

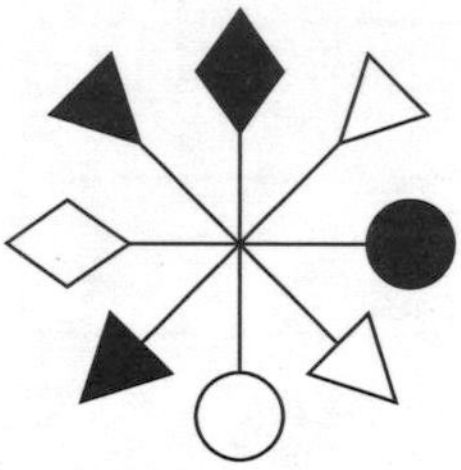

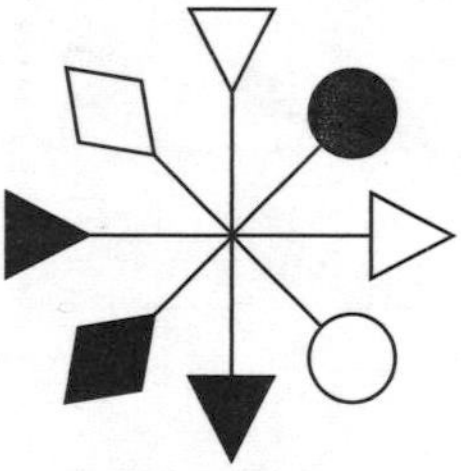

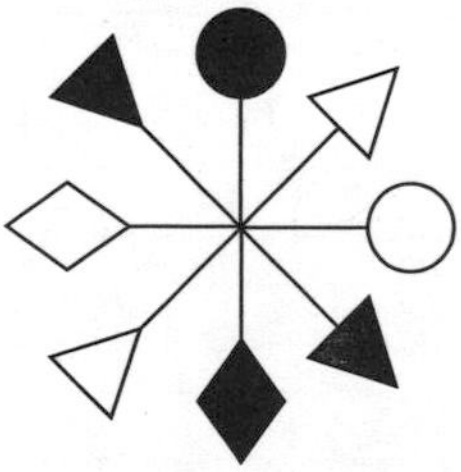

?

A

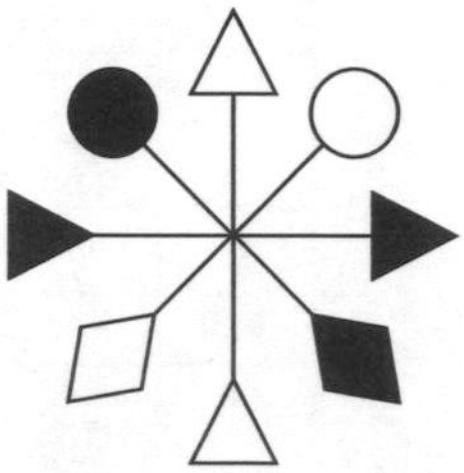

B

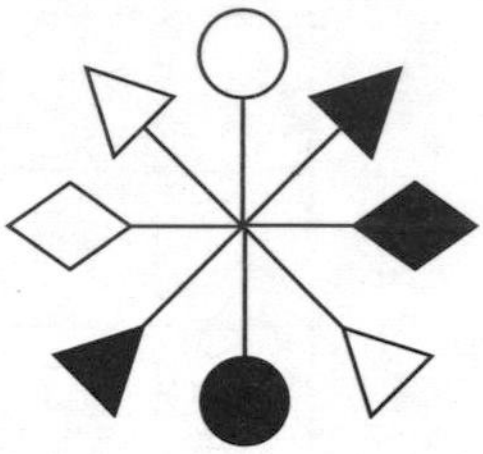

C

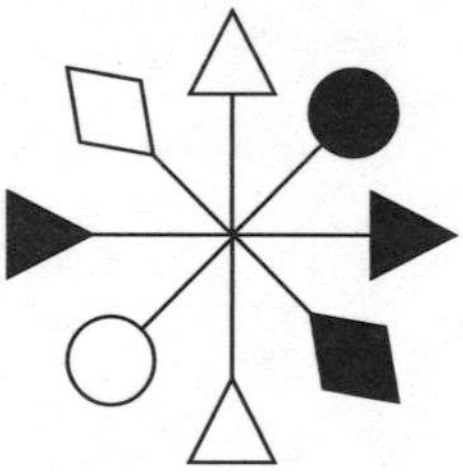

D

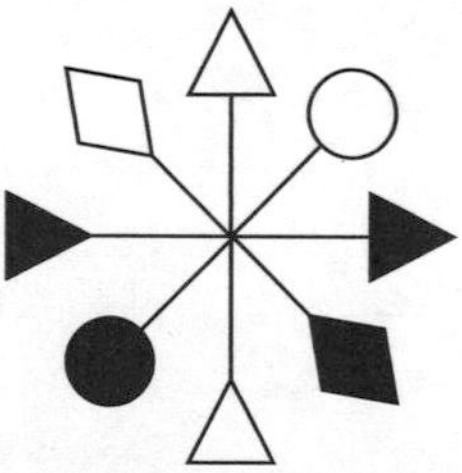

E

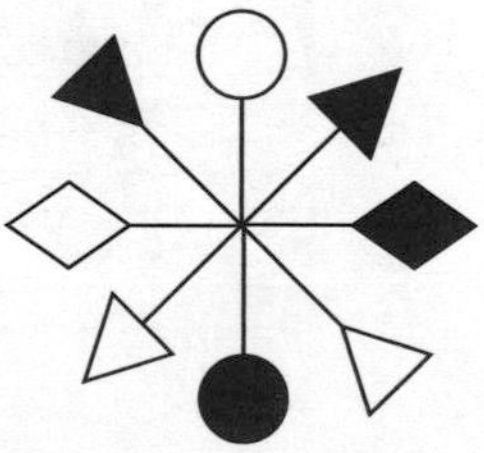

Mary has a certain distance to travel from home by car.

If she leaves home and drives at a constant speed of 90 km per hour, she knows that she will arrive five minutes early.

If she leaves home and drives at a constant speed of 75 km per hour, she knows that she will arrive six minutes late.

How far away from Mary's home is her destination?

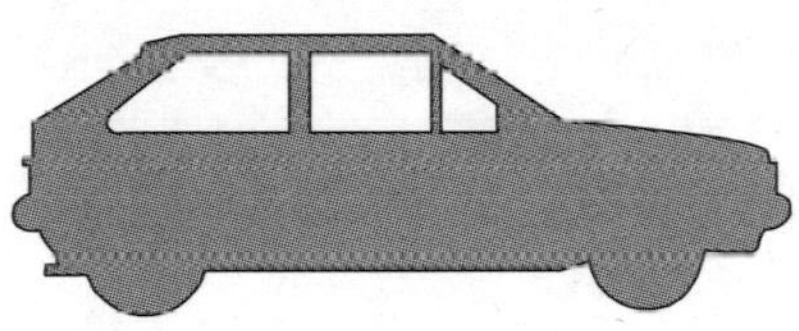

'One day ladies will take their computers for walks in the park and tell each other, "My little computer said such a funny thing this morning".'

What number should replace the question mark?

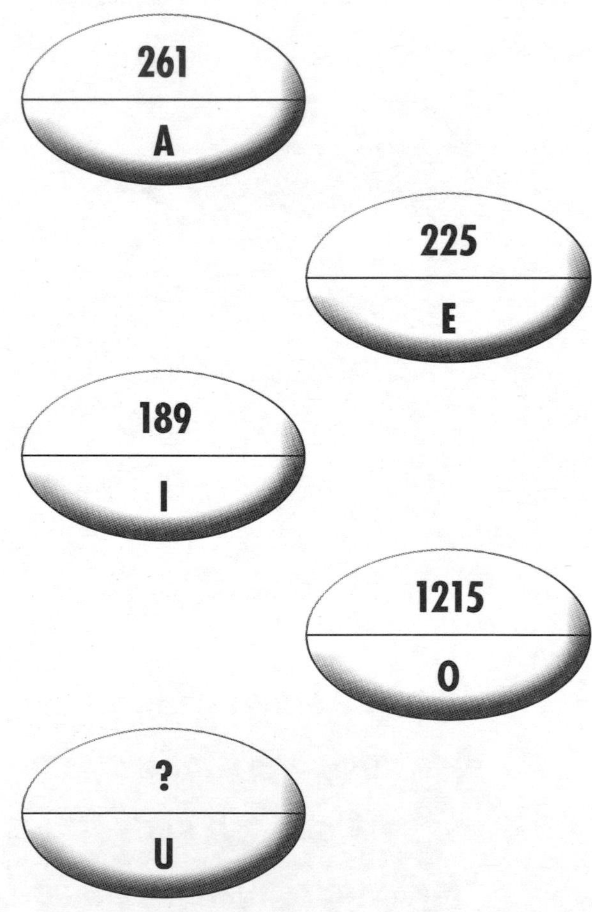

What number should replace the question mark?

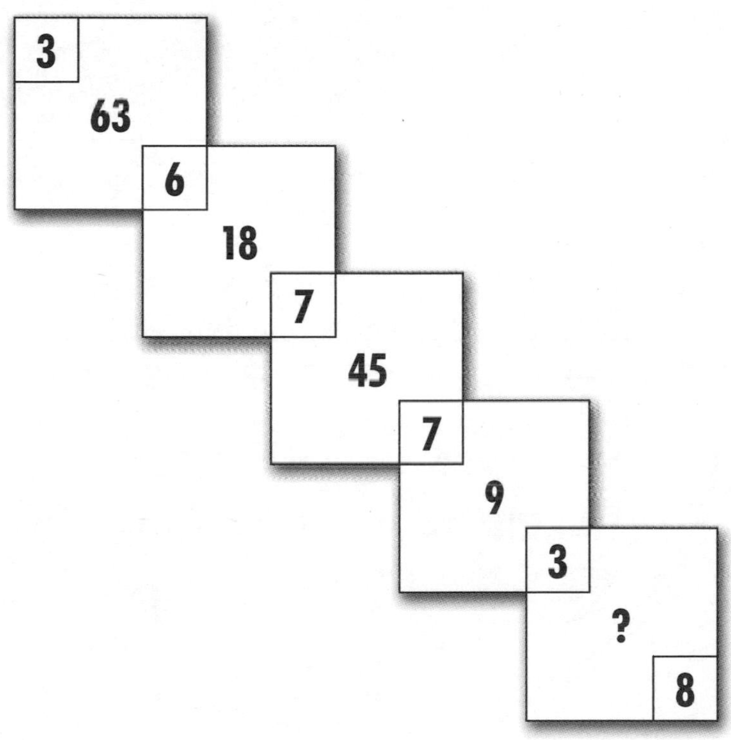

What single-digit numbers should replace the question marks?

What number should replace the question mark?

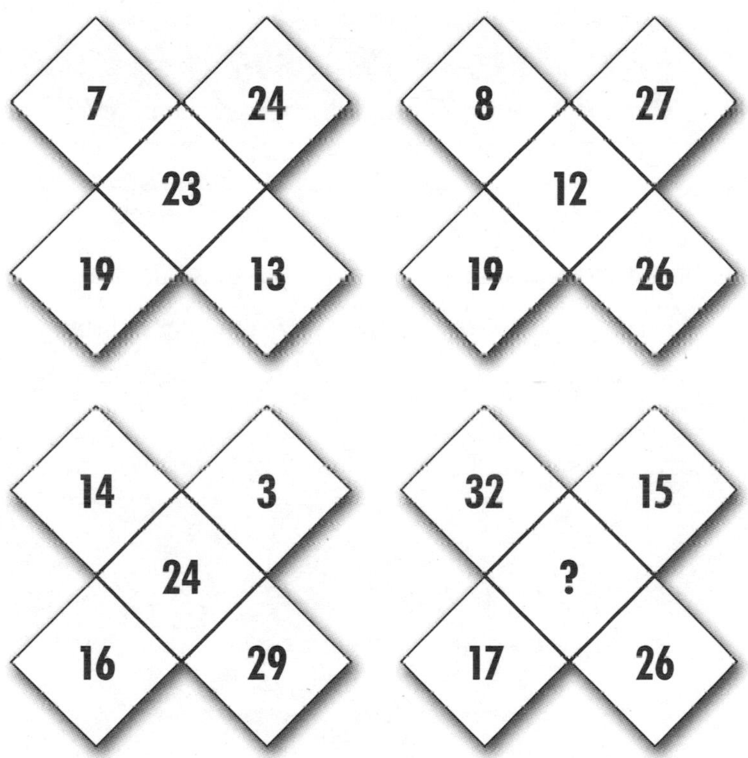

What number should replace the question mark?

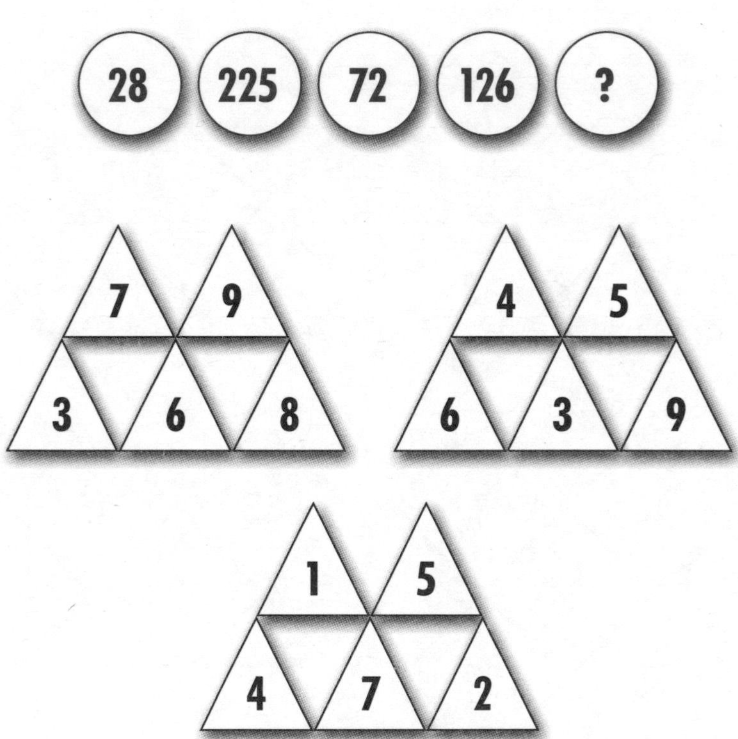

What letter should replace the question mark?

		6	N	8		
	11	4	S	13	1	
8	3	1	O	15	3	1
	13	3	?	6	5	
		8	P	8		

What letter should replace the question mark?

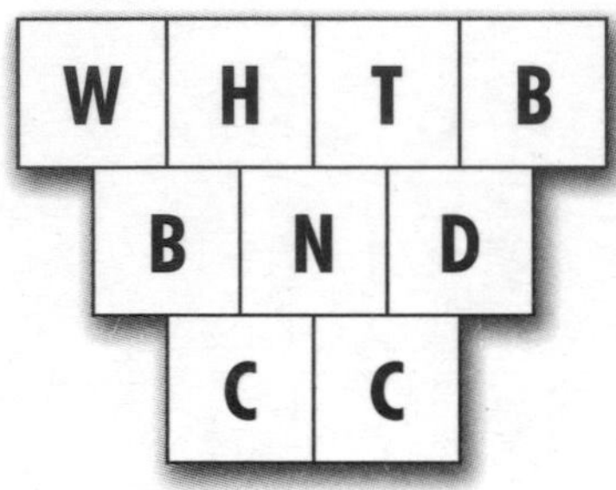

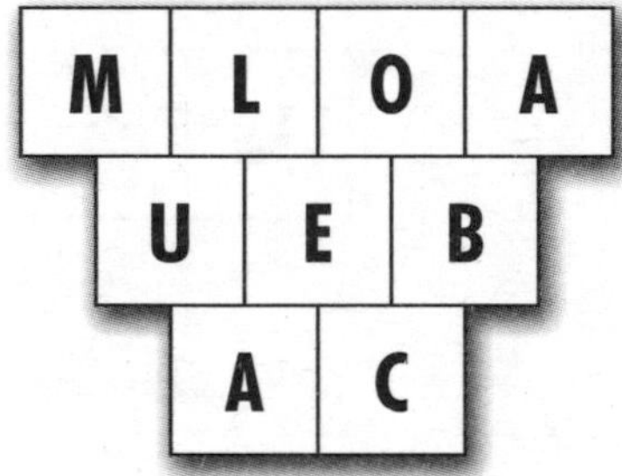

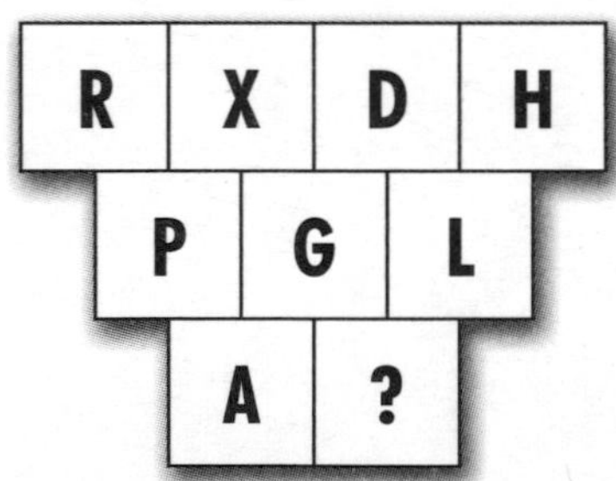

What number should replace the question mark?

256164096

324185832

169132197

225153375

196142744

28917491?

What number should replace the question mark?

2	4	10	13	7
6	22	19	20	1
3	13	?	20	9
2	17	5	4	6
4	13	17	18	8

The clock below is an electric clock, and needs no winding.

On the first day of May, it was set to the correct time: 8:30 in the morning. However, the clock gains ten minutes every 24 hours, and although it was viewed at 8:30 every morning, no-one put it right.

At 8:30 one morning, it showed the following time:

What was the earliest date on which it could have shown this time?

The Academy Award winning 2014 film *The Imitation Game* is primarily based on Alan Turing's work at Bletchley Park.

What numbers should replace the question marks?

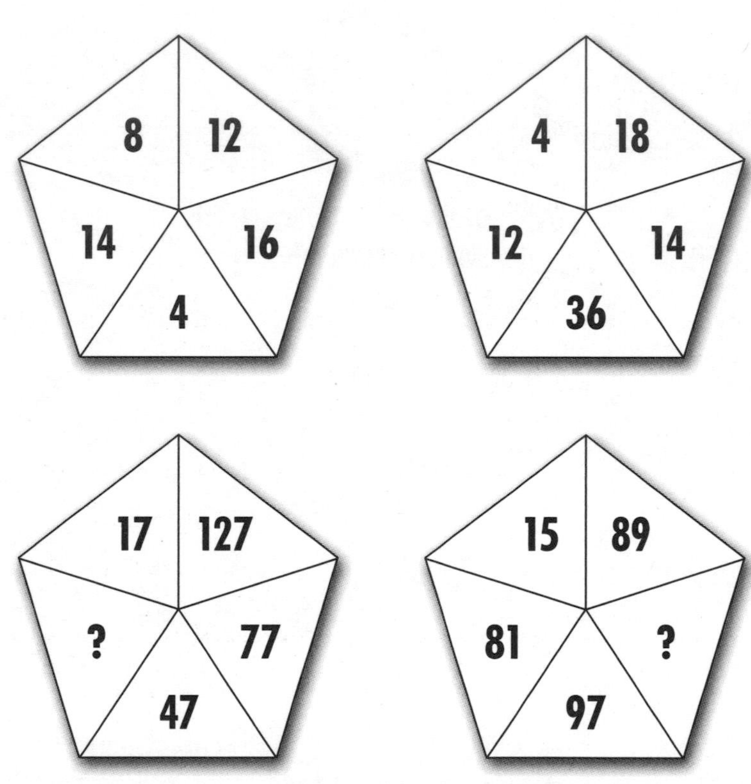

What number should replace the question mark?

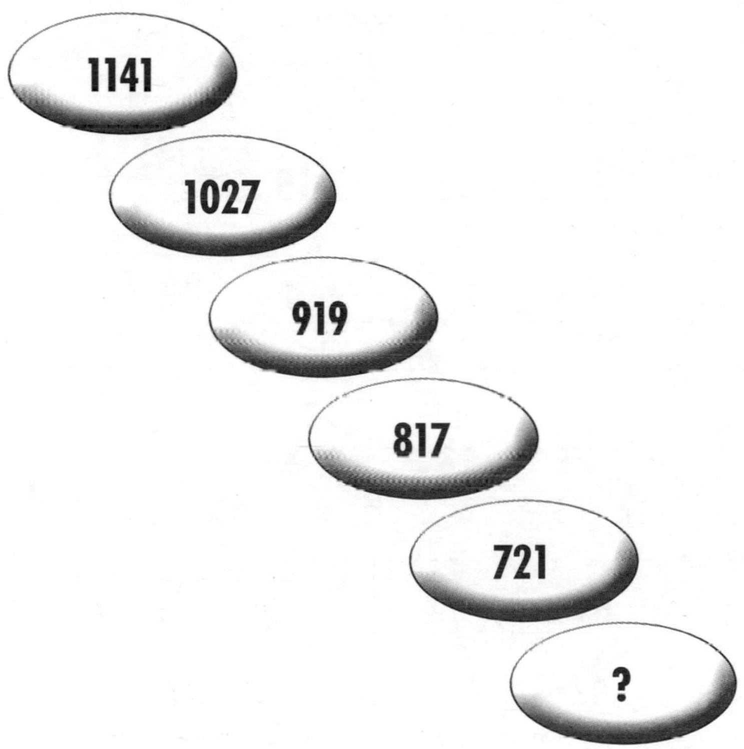

What numbers should replace the question marks?

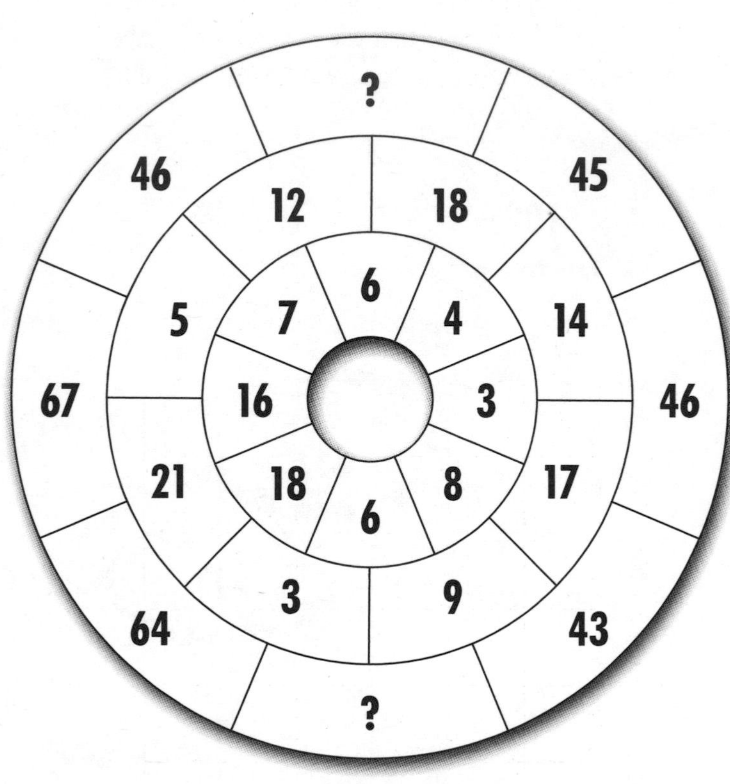

Place the numbers 1 to 6 into each row and column, one number per square. Each number represents a skyscraper of that many floors.

Arrange the skyscrapers in such a way that the given number outside the grid represents the number of buildings which can be seen from that point, looking only at that number's row or column.

A skyscraper with a lower number of floors cannot hide a higher building, but one with a higher number of floors always hides any lower building behind it.

	3		**5**			**2**	
							4
3							
4							**3**
1							**5**
2							**2**
				3	**1**	**2**	

What numbers should replace the question marks?

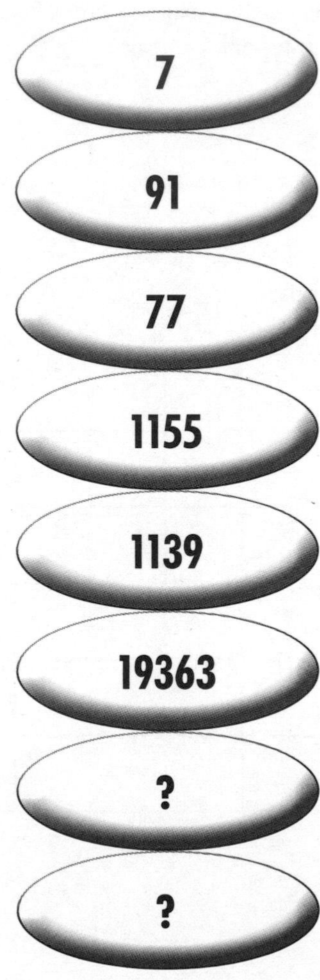

What number should replace the question mark?

5	46	87	2
3	210	160	7
1	370	360	9
2	17	55	4
6	137	?	3

What numbers should replace the question marks?

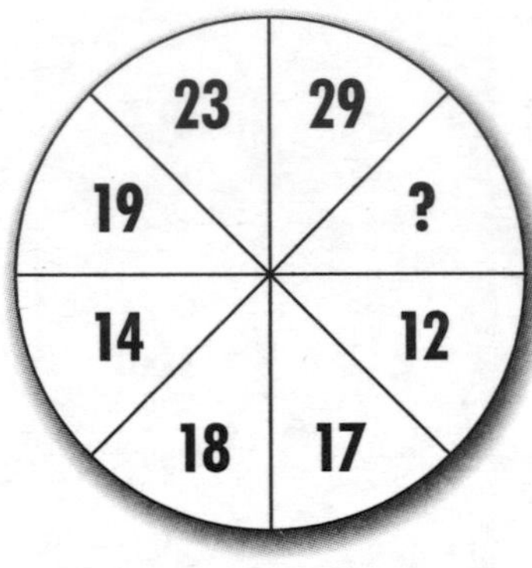

What number should replace the question mark?

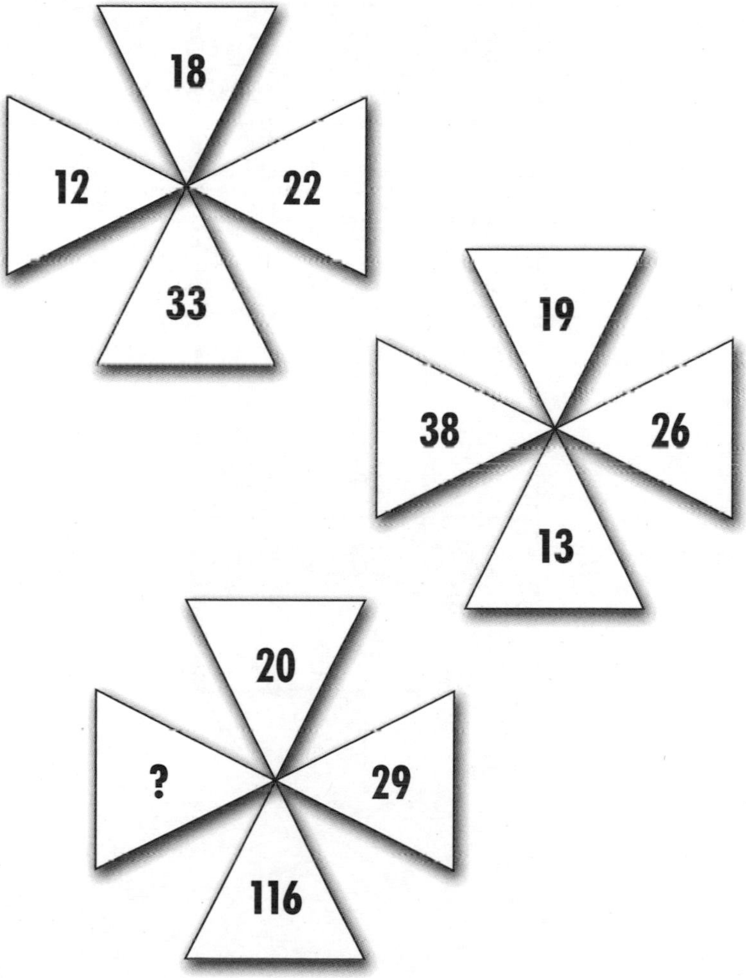

18
12 22
33

19
38 26
13

20
? 29
116

What number should replace the question mark?

36	17	153
16	22	88
21	24	126
18	32	144
12	13	39
8	34	68
26	20	130
15	44	?

103

What number should replace the question mark?

1584

2028

2548

3150

3840

4624

5508

?

What letter should replace the question mark?

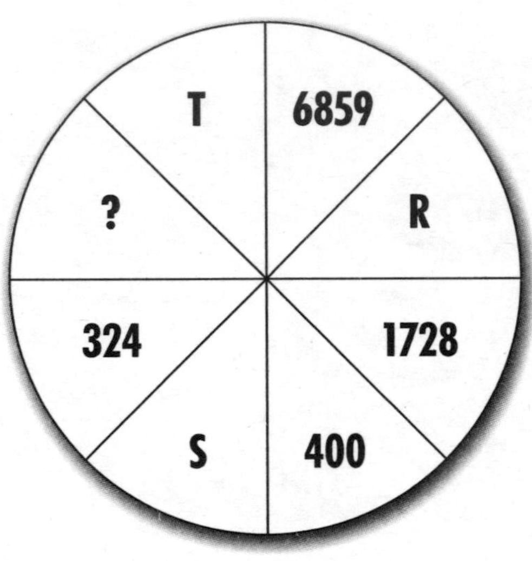

What number should replace the question mark?

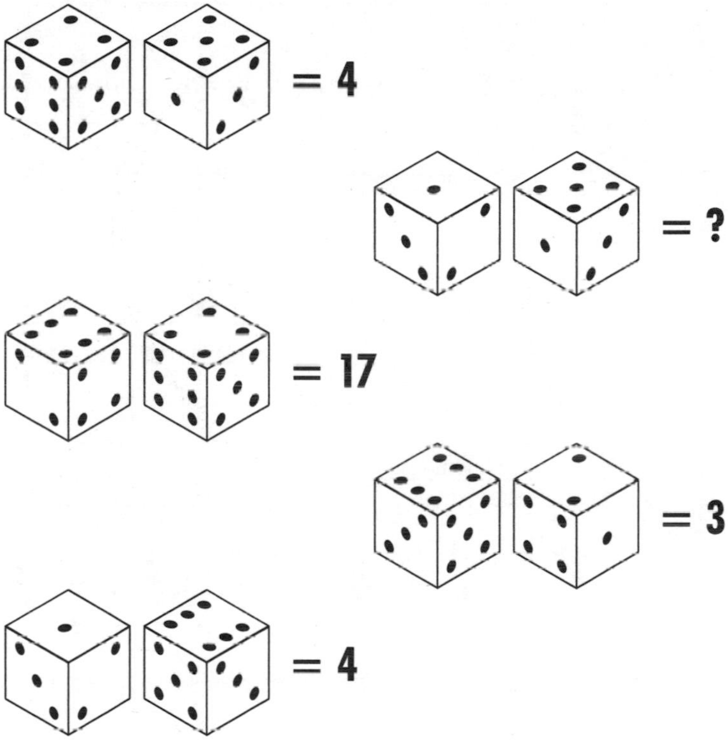

= 4

= ?

= 17

= 3

= 4

What number should replace the question mark?

7 / 8	9 5 13	6 / 6
5 3 13		4 ? 9
2 / 4	11 7 5	8 / 9

What letter should replace the question mark?

C	G	K
O	S	W
A	E	I

E	I	M
Q	U	Y
C	G	K

F	J	N
R	V	Z
D	H	L

D	H	L
P	T	X
B	F	?

What number should replace the question mark?

80		8	2	15
120		12		4
24		4		6
60		?		20
30	16	96		4

What number should replace the question mark?

7	2	9	3
2	4	7	6
2	3	4	8
6	5	8	7
?	5	6	9

What number should replace the question mark?

GK	IF
49	20

EH	MF
0	56

BK	PC
4	32

SD	KE
42	?

What number should replace the question mark?

B	C	A
K	M	E
L	N	J
P	R	O
U	W	T
X	Z	V
=	=	=
22	19	?

What number should replace the question mark?

10 + 9 = 52
8 + 7 = 36
6 + 5 = 24
4 + 3 = 12
2 + 1 = ?

What number should replace the question mark?

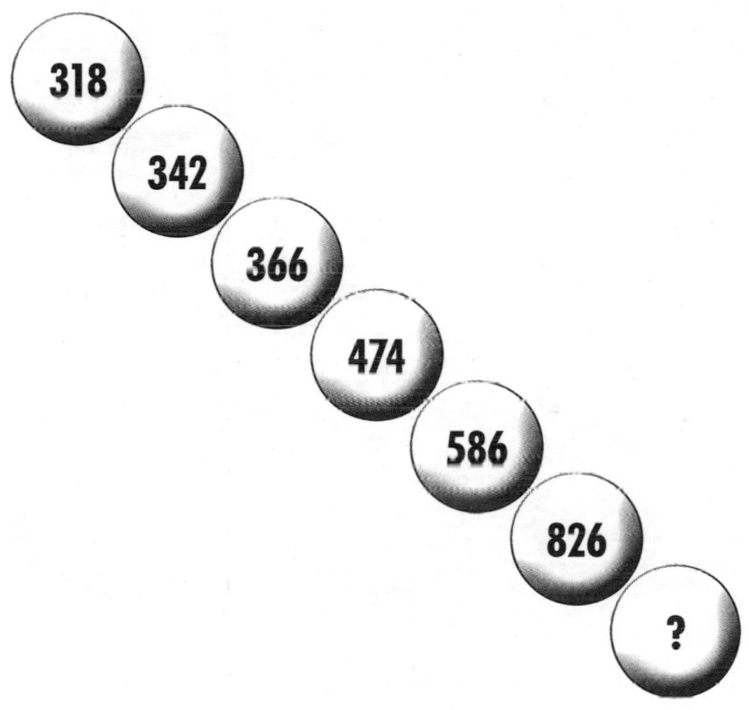

What numbers should replace the question marks?

12	36	?
10	22	38
9	15	23
8.5	11.5	15.5
8.25	9.75	?

What numbers should replace the question marks?

1	1	1	5	1	6	5
1	3	1	4	1	8	2
1	5	1	3	1	9	5
?	?	?	?	?	?	?
1	9	1	1	2	0	9
2	1	1	0	2	1	0

Given that scales A, B, and C balance perfectly, how many diamonds are needed to balance scale D?

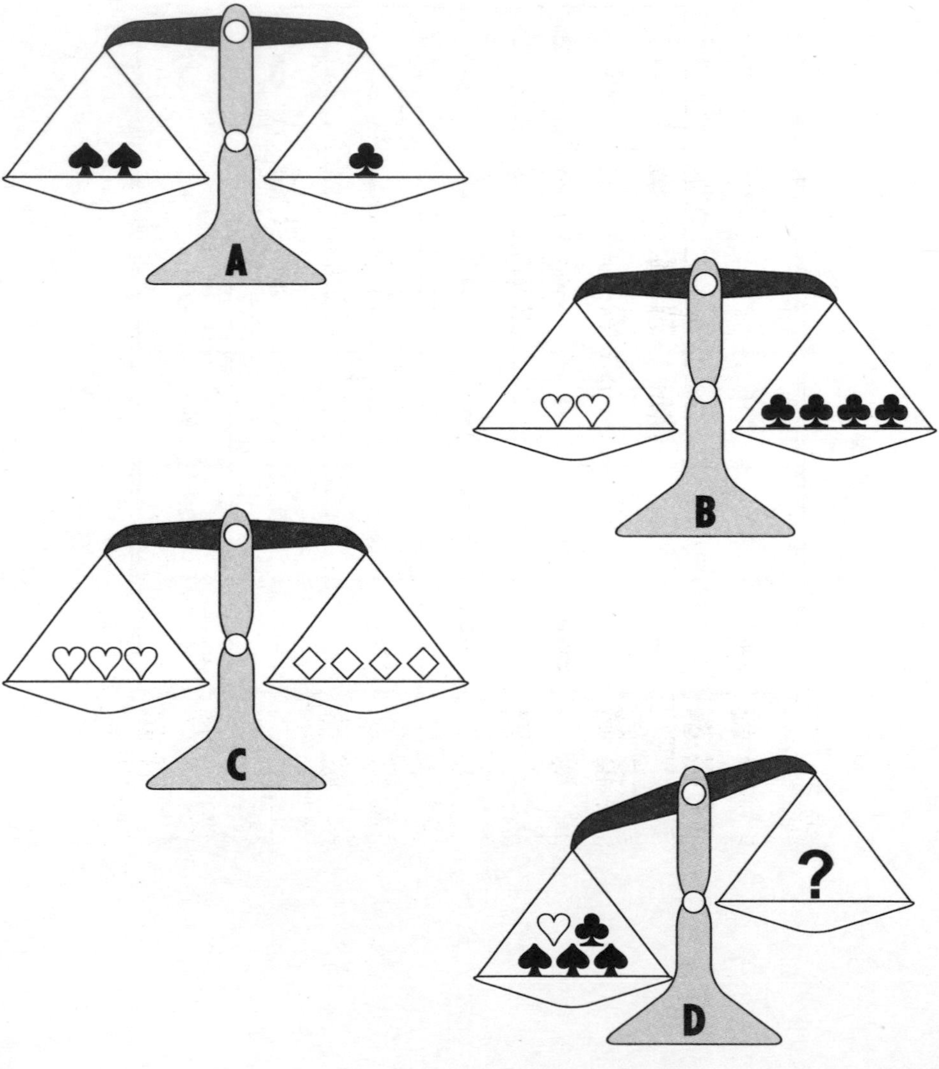

Which of the alternatives (A, B, C, or D)
should replace the question mark?

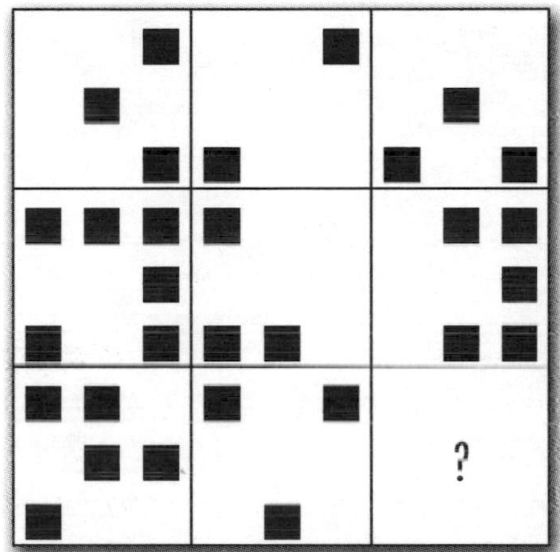

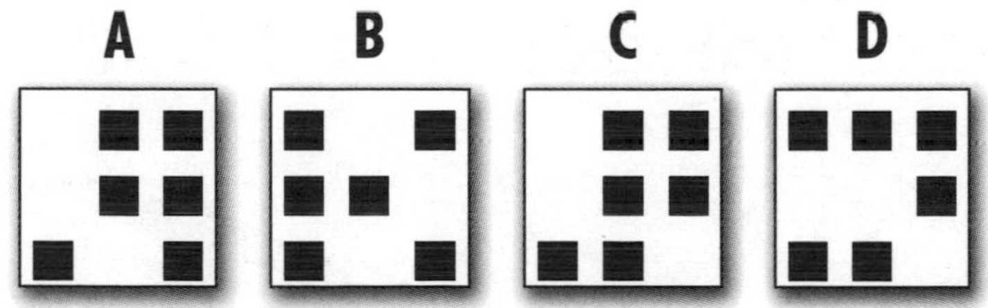

What number should replace the question mark?

T	7993

C	3

N	2731

H	493

Q	4903

E	103

P	4085

S	?

What number should replace the question mark?

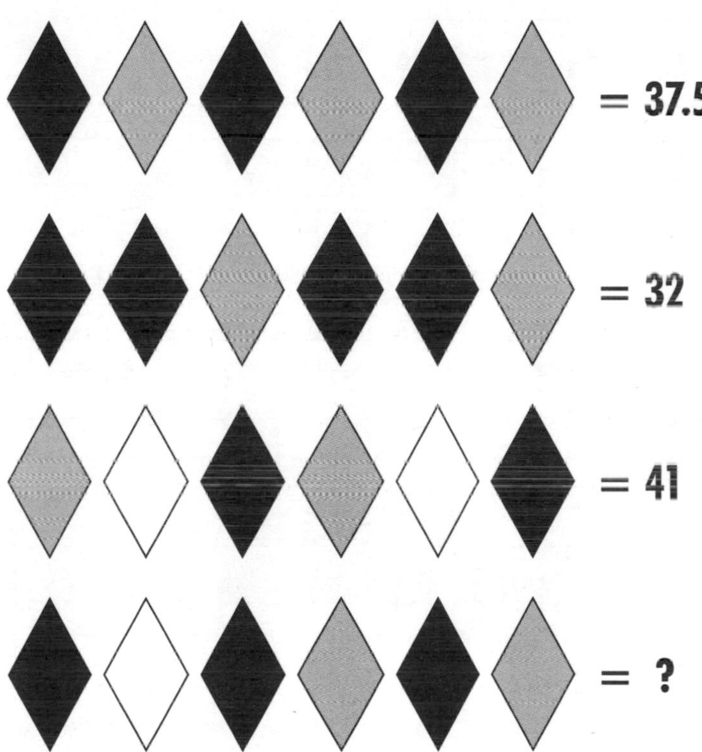

What numbers should replace the question marks?

66	43	34	39	33			
78	55	57	48	28	22		
76	67	69	46	37	42	36	
85	90	81	58	60	51	31	25
105	99	79	70	72	49	40	45
	94	88	93	84	61	63	54
		108	102	82	73	75	52
			?	91	?	87	?

What number should replace the question mark?

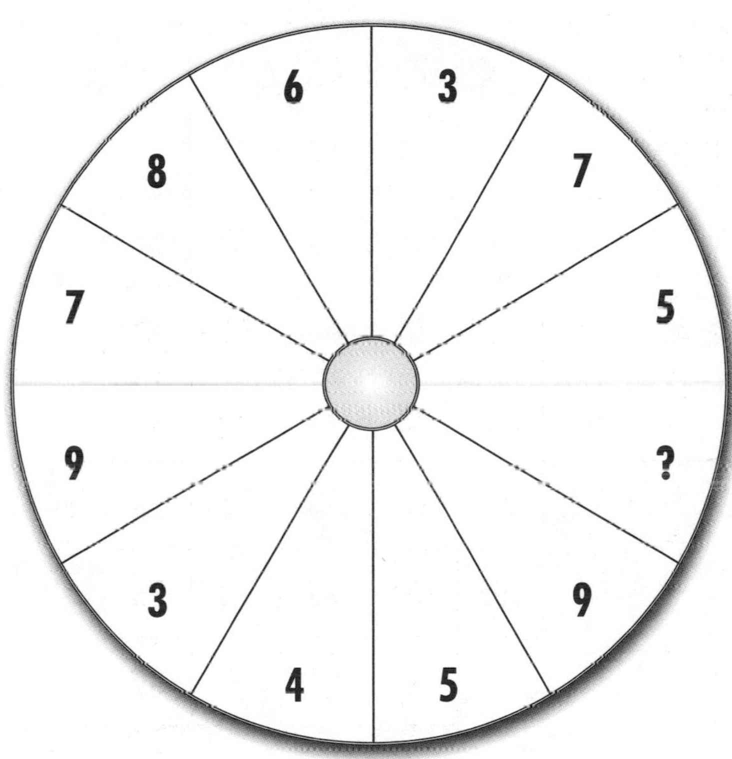

What number should replace the question mark?

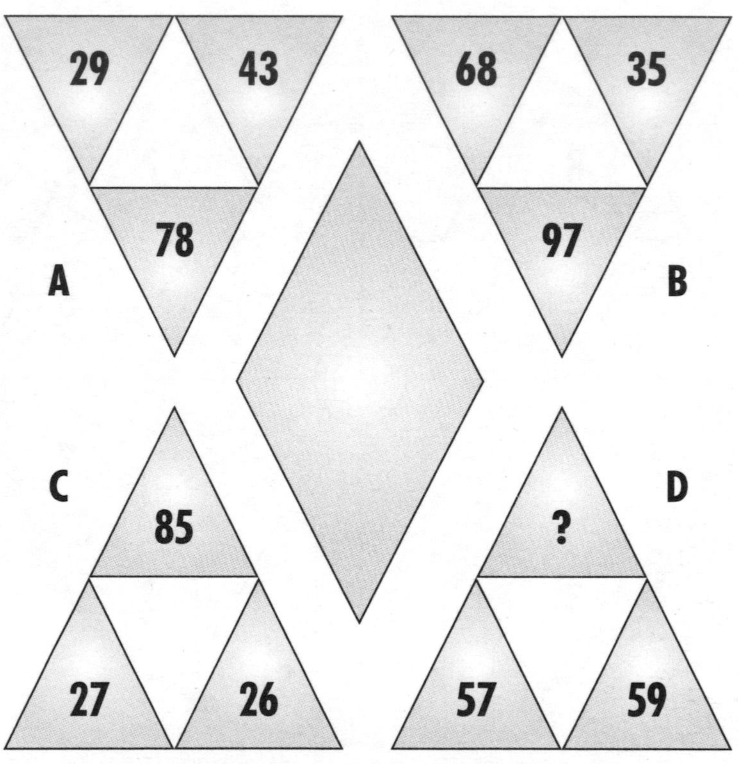

What number should replace the question mark?

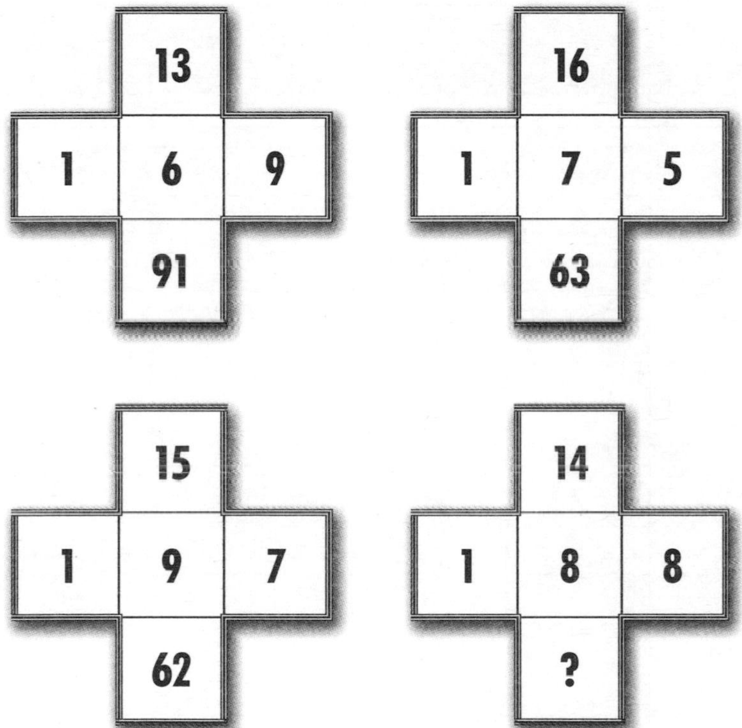

What numbers should replace the question marks?

5	7	3	1
6	8	5	4
7	6	4	1
8	8	7	6
9	7	?	?

What number should replace the question mark?

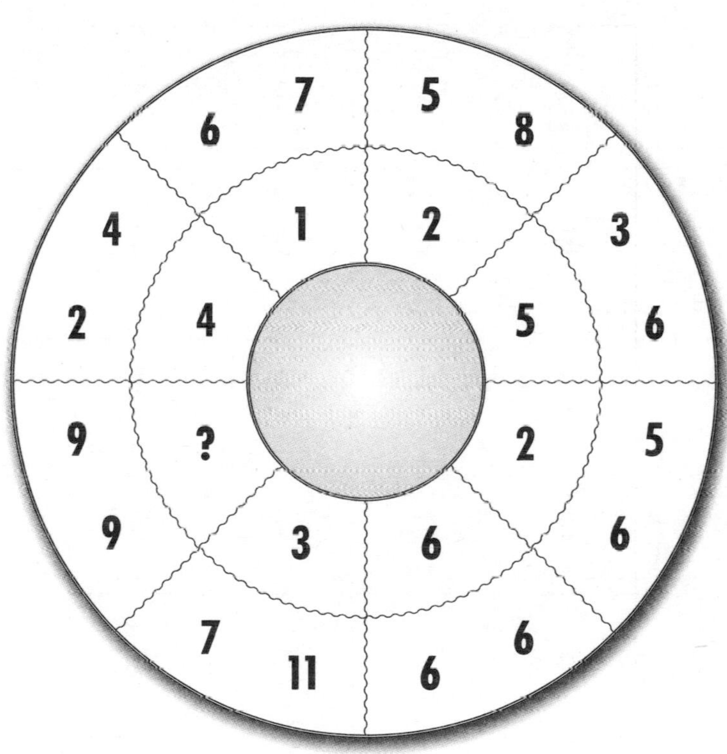

What number should replace the question mark?

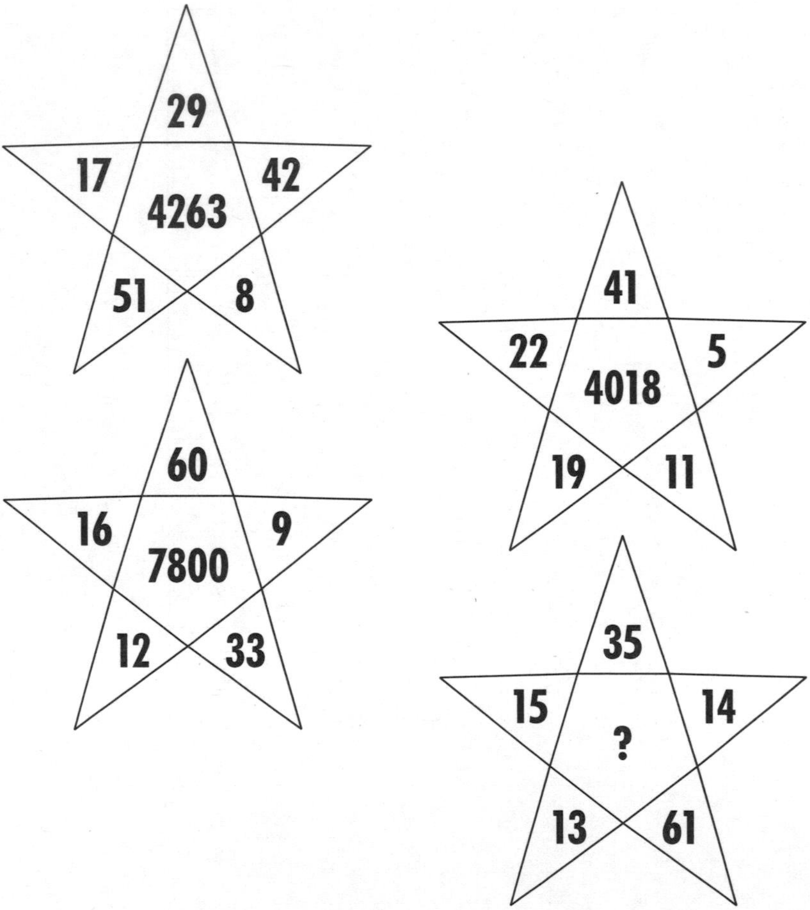

29
17 42
4263
51 8

41
22 5
4018
19 11

60
16 9
7800
12 33

35
15 14
?
13 61

What numbers should replace the question marks?

?	46
32	22

41	?
21	10

J	S
U	G

M	Z
F	D

Q	E
N	R

K	T
L	C

What letters should replace the question marks?

I	F	J	H	C	?
F	D	H	G	B	A
A	C	F	E	B	D
X	F	P	T	?	R
C	F	U	?	L	R
P	H	T	?	L	D

What letters should replace the question marks?

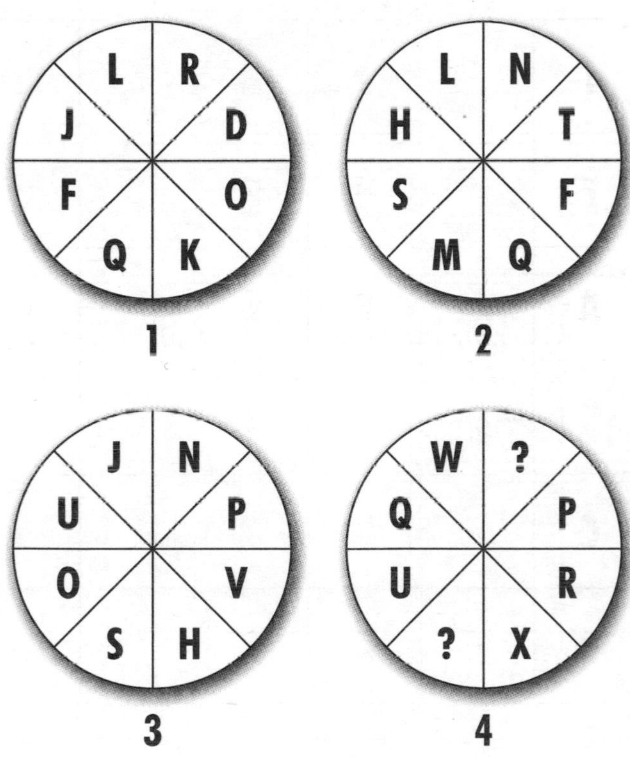

The blank cells below should be filled with numbers, any of which may occur more than once.

Numbers in every row multiply to the totals on the right, as do the two long diagonal lines; those in every column multiply to the totals along the bottom.

				104.04
	2.10		9.00	23.625
	3.00	0.50	7.10	23.96
4.00	6.80	0.90		4.90
			6.00	6.12
7.65	25.70	1.125	76.68	4.05

What number should replace the question mark?

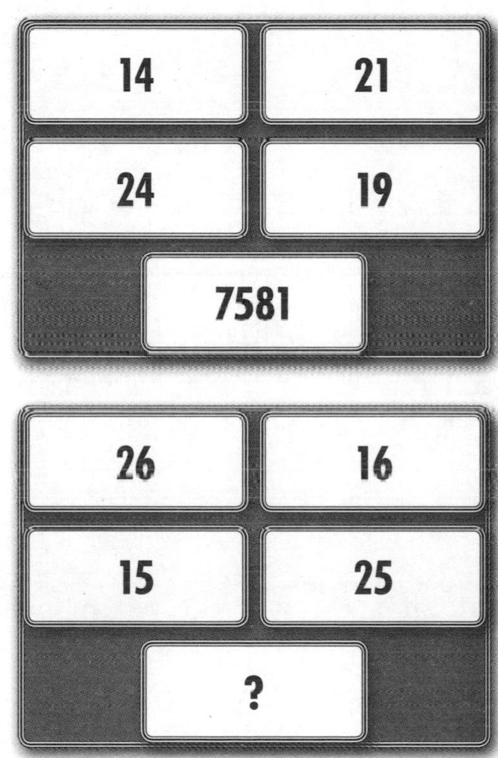

Whole numbers (not fractions of numbers) from 1 to 26 have been replaced by different letters of the alphabet. The sums below will enable you to crack the code. The letter V does not appear in the clues below, although its value can be determined by eliminating all other possibilities.

Write the correct number beneath each letter in the answer box.

1. A x B = C

2. D + E = F

3. G x A = H

4. H + I = E

5. A x J = K

6. L x M = N

7. M x O = P

8. Q x A = R

9. Q + N = P

10. S + Q = U

11. T + E = U

12. A x N = W

13. X = O + Q

14. X x A = Y

15. T + J = Z

A	B	C	D	E	F	G	H

I	J	K	L	M	N	O	P	Q

R	S	T	U	V	W	X	Y	Z

What numbers should replace the question marks?

7 6
6 9
9 3
5 4

8 8
3 6
2 7
9 5

20 45
21 18
? 18
48 56

9 14
10 11
15 9
14 ?

Four cogs similar to the one shown have different numbers of teeth, and each rotates at a different speed to any of the others.

The black tooth on each cog was at the top both before they started to rotate, and when they stopped rotating. Each movement of the black tooth is to a position one tooth pitch clockwise, so in the case of the cog below which has 20 teeth, it would take 20 movements to reach the position from which it started.

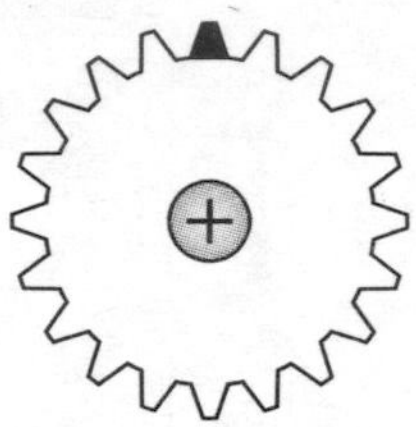

Cog A has 110 teeth and made five full rotations before stopping, at a rate of one tooth pitch every 2.0 seconds.

Cog B has 120 teeth and made six full rotations before stopping, at a rate of one tooth pitch every 1.5 seconds.

Cog C has 115 teeth and made seven full rotations before stopping, at a rate of one tooth pitch every 2.5 seconds.

Cog D has 105 teeth and made eight full rotations, at a rate of one tooth pitch every 1.25 seconds.

All four cogs started rotating at the same time. Which cog was first to finish rotating?

In order to make the sums correct, replace each of the ten symbols with one different digit from 0 to 9, that digit remaining the same wherever the symbol occurs.

Two have already been replaced with the digits '3' and '0', so begin by replacing all instances of those symbols with '3' and '0'.

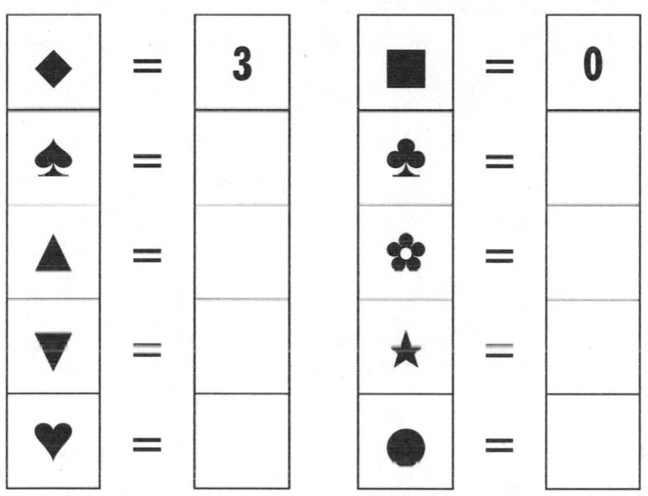

✿● minus ◆ equals ♥

▼ multiplied by ● equals ✿♣

♣ multiplied by ✿● equals ♣♠

♣ plus ✿● equals ✿★

✿★ multiplied by ◆ equals ♣♠

▲ multiplied by ✿● equals ★■

What number should replace the question mark?

1

9

There are two sets of numbers in each shape: the cube followed by the square of the same number. From the top these are the cubes/squares of 3, 4, 5, 6, and 7 (7^3 = 343 and 7^2 = 49).

2

Middle = 196, bottom left = 7

Divide the top number by the bottom right number to obtain the central number, and divide the central number by the bottom right number to obtain the bottom left number.

3

11:00 a.m.

The clock was set at one o'clock this morning, and lost four minutes per hour, so (the hands having moved 7½ hours) it had lost 30 minutes. Therefore at the time it stopped, it was actually nine o'clock. Nine o'clock was two hours before it was checked again, so the clock was checked at 11 o'clock.

4

6,550 sq cm

Base: 30 x 40 = 1,200 sq cm, top surfaces: 30 x 40 = 1,200 sq cm, sides = 35 x 30 = 1,050 sq cm – 15 x 25 (375) = 675 sq cm x 2 = 1,350 sq cm; back and front = 35 x 40 = 1,400 sq cm x 2 = 2,800 sq cm.

5

B

From top to bottom in each set, every shape moves one square at a time as follows: white circles move diagonally down, white crosses move up, white squares move right to left, black circles move down, black crosses move diagonally up, and black squares move left to right, returning to the start when the end of a row or column is reached.

6

Cog B = 7, Cog C = 4

Moves:	Cog A	Cog B	Cog C
First	6	8	8
Second	9	5	4
Third	3	6	3
Fourth	8	9	6
Fifth	5	4	9
Sixth	7	7	2
Seventh	2	2	1
Eighth	4	4	8
Ninth	1	7	4

7

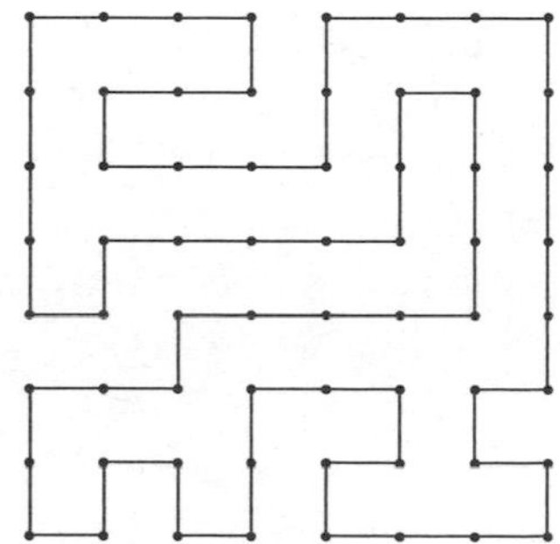

8

123

Starting at the top and moving clockwise, add each number to the sum total of its digits to obtain the next number: 120 + 3 (1 + 2 + 0) = 123.

9

Outside 86 metres, inside 74 metres

The outside perimeter has 35 two-metre faces (70 metres) and 16 one-metre faces (16 metres), thus a total of 86 metres: the inside perimeter has 28 two-metre faces (56 metres) and 18 one-metre faces (18 metres), thus a total of 74 metres.

10

F

Read top to bottom each of the others has a matching set of numbers in reverse (A and D, B and H, C and I, E and G).

11

83

Multiply together the two left numbers and divide the top right number by the bottom right number, then deduct the second result from the first to obtain the number in the central square: 6 x 15 = 90, 21 ÷ 3 = 7, 90 – 7 = 83.

12

13

14

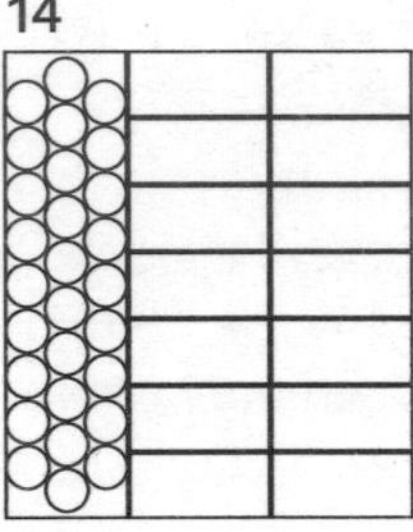

14

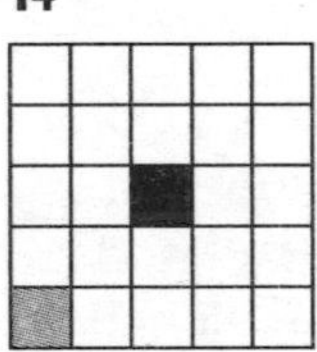

15

3059

From the top, each number is the result of adding consecutive pairs of cube numbers (1 + 8 = 9, 27 + 64 = 91, etc), so 1331 + 1728 = 3059.

16

38

From the top, add the first number to half of the second number, one third of the third number, and one quarter of the fourth, to obtain the fifth number.

17

★ = 26 ✚ = 15 ▲ = 5 ● = 61

■ = 17

18

0			O	1		1	O		0
								O	
O				1	O			2	O
		0				O	2		1
1	O		■	1	0		O		
		1	1	O		1	2	O	
		O	■			O			
					O				
O						0			0
	0	1	O		0		O		

19

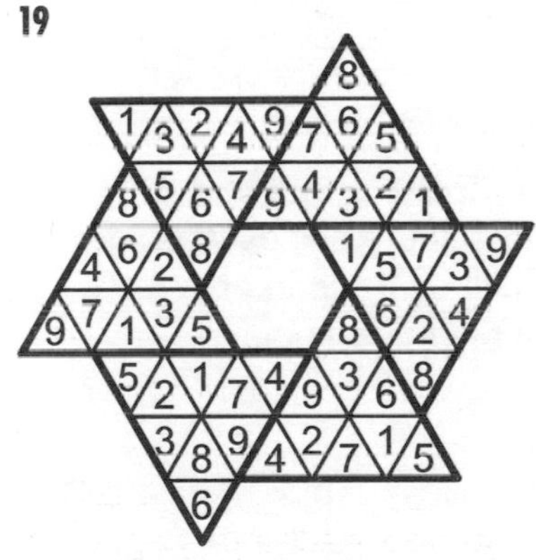

20

N

The sum total of the values of the letters to the right and left is equal to the reverse alphanumerical value of the letter in the middle: F (6) + G (7) = N (13).

21

D

22

756

Multiply together the numbers In the left triangle, then halve the result to give the number in the right triangle: 9 x 8 x 21 = 1512 ÷ 2 = 756.

23

573 revolutions

The perimeter of the room is (5 + 5 + 4 + 4) 18 metres. 18 x 3 = 54 metres (54,000 mm). The diameter of the ball is 30 mm, so its circumference is 94.26 mm: 30 x π (3.142). 54,000 ÷ 94.26 = 572.884, or 573 to the nearest whole number.

24

I

The difference between the values of the top left letter and the bottom letter is twice that of the difference between the top right letter and the bottom letter.

25

Top left = 128, middle = 4096, bottom right = 8

The top number is the result of multiplying the far right number and right bottom number; the far left number is the result of multiplying the two bottom numbers, the central number is the result of multiplying the top number and far left number: 4 x 8 = 32, 8 x 16 = 128, 32 x 128 = 4096.

26

O	X	X	X	O	O	X	X	X
X	O	X	O	X	X	O	X	X
O	X	X	X	O	X	O	O	O
O	X	O	O	O	X	O	O	X
X	O	X	X	X	O	X	O	X
O	X	X	O	X	O	X	X	X
X	X	O	O	X	X	O	O	O
O	O	X	X	O	X	O	O	X
X	X	O	O	X	O	X	X	X
X	O	O	O	X	O	X	O	O
O	X	O	O	X	O	O	X	X
X	O	X	X	O	X	O	O	X
X	O	X	O	O	X	O	X	X
O	O	X	X	X	O	X	O	O
X	X	O	O	X	O	X	X	X
O	O	X	X	X	O	O	X	O
X	X	O	O	O	X	X	X	O

27

B

Both black and the white squares move from the middle to a corner and back to the middle; when they go to a corner, it is next clockwise from the corner which that square had occupied before.

28

414

Multiply together the numbers in the left quarters of each circle, then add five to obtain the number in the top right quarter; multiply all three numbers together to obtain the number in the bottom right quarter.

29

8.4

The sum total of the values of each pair of letters is multiplied by three then divided by ten to obtain the number in each set.

30

31

264

Multiply together the three numbers in the circles, then divide the result by three to obtain the number in the triangle.

32

White circle = J, black circle = Q

Starting at the top and spiralling in a clockwise direction towards the middle following the white circles and missing two letters of the alphabet between each letter. At the middle, spiral back outwards in an anticlockwise (counterclockwise) direction, following the black circles and missing two letters between each.

33

16

The answer is the total number of straight lines in the letters in the name that are formed only by straight lines.

34

14

The numbers in the two outer triangles are multiplied together to equal the sum total of the two central numbers.

35

E

From top to bottom in each set, two is added to each number in the top row, three is added to each number in the middle row, and four is added to each number in the bottom row, then the whole square makes a quarter turn clockwise to arrive at the next set.

36

1	6	3	4	5	2
2	5	4	6	1	3
4	3	6	5	2	1
5	1	2	3	6	4
6	4	1	2	3	5
3	2	5	1	4	6

37

823

Multiply together the two numbers at the bottom of each shape; the result is four higher than the sum total of the two numbers at the top: 131 x 13 = 1703 – 4 = 1699 = 823 + 876.

38

From the left: second column = 8, fourth column = 39

The number in the second column is the difference between the two numbers to the left and right; the number in the fourth column is the difference between the two numbers in the first and second columns.

39

4

Five spades weigh the same as 2 diamonds and a heart (scale A). So substitute the 5 spades in scale B with 2 diamonds and a heart; thus 2 hearts weigh the same as 4 diamonds, so one heart weighs the same as 2 diamonds. Substitute the heart in scale A with 2 diamonds, so that 4 diamonds weigh the same as 5 spades. In scale C there are 4 diamonds and 5 spades, so substitute the 5 spades with 4 diamonds; thus giving 8 diamonds in scale C. Four diamonds weigh the same as 2 hearts (above), so 4 hearts are needed to balance scale C.

40

2052

The number in the square is the square of the first two digits in the circle plus the cube of the second two digits in the circle: $18^2 = 324$, $12^3 = 1728$, 324 + 1728 = 2052.

41

10

Multiply the numbers in the top two hexagons, multiply the numbers in the central two hexagons, take the second result from the first to obtain a number that is the multiple of the numbers in the bottom two hexagons: 6 x 8 = 48, 2 x 9 = 18, 48 – 18 = 30 = 10 x 3.

42

A

43

Pump C

6,750 litres per hour = 112.5 litres per minute = 5,062.5 litres in 45 minutes.

44

8 below N, 0 below T

The value of each letter is multiplied by its reverse alpha-numerical value, leading to a three-digit number:
N = 14 x 13 = 182, T = 20 x 7 = 140.

45

From the top:

13, D, 7, L, 25, A, 14, P

The reverse values of the letters in each row all appear somewhere in the row above. From top to bottom, these are 13 (for N), D (for 23), 7 (for T), L (for 15), 25 (for B), A (for 26), 14 (for M), and P (for 11).

46

339

In each row, multiply together the numbers in the circles, then add together the numbers in the circles, adding the two results to obtain the number in the square: 19 x 16 = 304, 19 + 16 = 35, 304 + 35 = 339.

47

115 sq mm

A: π x radius² (3.142 x 144) = 452.448 ÷ 4 (quarter circle) = 113.112; B = 38.49; A – B = 74.622; C = 9 x 9 = 81 ÷ 2 = 40.50; 74.622 + 40.50 = 115.122.

48

12

In each column, the sum total of the numbers in the central three squares is the same as the sum total of the numbers in the other four squares: 19 + 22 + 3 = 44,
9 + 16 + 7 + 12 = 44.

49

451

Multiply together the numbers in the two large sectors, then deduct 17 to obtain the number in the small sector: 26 x 18 = 468 – 17 = 451.

50

Clock A: 5:00 Clock B: 3:10

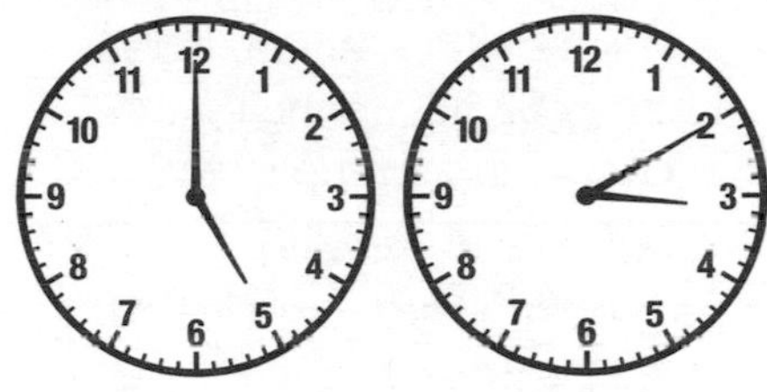

Clock A moves back two hours every hour, and clock B moves forward 20 minutes per hour. In 9½ hours from 12.00, clock A will have moved back 19 hours, and clock B will have moved forwards 3 hours and 10 minutes.

51

81.25%

52 ÷ 64 = 0.8125, 0.8125 x 100 = 81.25%.

52

R

Multiply the value of the letter at the left by the value of the central letter, then deduct the value of the central letter to obtain the value of the letter at the right: 7 (G) x 3 (C) = 21 - 3 = 18 (R).

53

17.844 kg

Steel = 2.462 m^2 x 4.6 kg = 11.325 kg, perspex = 1.230 m^2 x 5.3 kg = 6.519 kg, 11.325 kg + 6.519 kg = 17.844 kg.

54

D and G

55

Left outer = 84, left inner = 6, right inner = 9, right outer = 66

A number in the middle circle is the sum total of the two numbers in the sectors they touch in the inner circle. A number in the outer circle is the sum total of the numbers in the two sectors they touch in the middle circle multiplied by two.

56

A

Each of the smallest squares moves to a corner one place anticlockwise (counterclockwise), then rotates 45 degrees.

57

Top = 64, bottom right = 356

In each design, moving from the bottom left to the top, then down to the bottom right, deduct the second number from the first to obtain the third, deduct the fourth from the third to obtain the fifth, and deduct the sixth from the fifth to obtain the seventh: 759 – 315 = 444, 444 – 64 = 380, 380 – 24 = 356.

58

1417176

Multiply each number by the sum total of its digits to obtain the next number: 5 + 2 + 4 + 8 + 8 = 27 x 52488 = 1417176.

59

Middle = 21, right = 28

Multiply the two digits in the left sector to obtain the number in the right sector, then add these four digits together to obtain the central number: 7 x 4 = 28, 7 + 4 + 2 + 8 = 21.

60

180

Take the square number from the cube number according to the number of points each shape has. The missing number is on the six-point star, so 216 (6^3) – 36 (6^2) = 180.

61

P

The letters in each point of the top star are alphabetically half way between the two letters in corresponding points of the bottom stars.

62

C

From top left, follow the chain of shape sequences, down to the bottom right. At each stage, the shape at the top moves to the bottom, and the other shapes move up one place; as they do so, the shape previously at the top changes shade when it goes to the bottom: white changes to grey, grey changes to black, and black changes to white.

63

$8,120

The price of the car is $14,000, plus taxes of 18%, so the taxes amount to $2,520, bringing the total cost of the car up to $16,520. Peter's father will pay $5,600 (40% of $14,000) plus $2,520 (taxes), thus $8,120.

64

A

π x radius² x length gives the volumes:

A = 35,348, B = 21,551, C = 19,912.

65

	O	2	O	1	1	O			
O					0	2	O		
	1			0					
	O		1		O			O	
0			O		2	O		3	O
	1	O	2					O	
				O			1		
							O		
	O		0		O	1	2		
O	2		0				O		

66

R

The letters in the inner ring are the same number of letters from the start or end of the alphabet as the letters in the opposite sector in the outer ring. I is nine letters from the start, and R is nine letters from the end of the alphabet.

67

68

B

69

85

The number at the top is the total of the squares of the numbers at the bottom: 4 (2^2) + 81 (9^2) = 85.

70

W

Working down the columns, add the values of the first two letters then deduct four to get the value of the third letter, add the values of the second and third then deduct four to get the value of the fourth, add the values of the third and fourth then deduct four to get the value of the fifth letter.

71

117

The numbers in white rectangles are multiples of any two numbers in black rectangles, so the missing number is 117 (9 x 13).

72

504

Multiply together the sum total of the values of the letters, then multiply this total by nine to obtain the number: 8 (H) x 7 (G) = 56 x 9 = 504.

73

$9.35

One kilo of fish plus one kilo of potatoes costs $4.20, and the fish costs $2.30 more than the potatoes, Deduct $2.30 from $4.20 then divide by two to balance the result ($1.90) between the two different items ($0.95 each), so the potatoes are $0.95 per kilo, and the fish is ($2.30 + $0.95) $3.25 per kilo. Thus two kilos of fish cost $6.50, and three kilos of potatoes cost $2.85. Simon's bill was $6.50 + $2.85 = $9.35.

74

N and 56

The sum total of the top left and bottom right numbers is the cube of the value of the letter, which is equal to the multiple of the top right and bottom left numbers: N = 14, 14^3 = 2744, 1329 + 1415 = 2744, 49 x 56 = 2744.

75

150

E is the fifth letter of the alphabet: 5 cubed (125) + 5 squared (25) = 150.

76

5

Start at the top left square and spiral clockwise towards the middle, shading every third white square each time.

77

G

Each set on the left matches a set on the right that contains letters with reverse values to those on the left. From top to bottom, the first matches the third, the second matches the fourth, the third matches the second, and the fourth matches the first. T = 20, and G = 20 (reverse value).

78

A

Working from left to right in each row, and from top to bottom in each column, the circles in the third squares are black only where they have both been white in the first two squares.

79

15

Viewed as diagonal lines of numbers working from right to left from the top of the line each time, the sum total of the numbers in each is one higher than that of the sum total of the numbers in the line to its left and above it.

80

E

The internal design rotates anticlockwise (counterclockwise) 30 degrees, the square rotates 45 degrees, the arrows change to the opposite direction, and the black and white circles change places.

81

4

Reading left to right, the sequence is two stars, triangle, square (A); two triangles, square, star (B); two squares, star, triangle (C); then repeat this (A), (B), (C) sequence.

82

D

The shape at the top of each changes places with the shape at the far left and the whole design makes a 45 degree turn anticlockwise (counterclockwise).

83

82.5 kilometres

At 90 km per hour, Mary will travel 1.5 km per minute, so 82.5 km in 55 minutes. At 75 km per hour,

Mary will travel 1.25km per minute, so 82.5 km in 66 minutes.

84

621

The number above each letter is its reverse value followed by its value:

U = 6 and 21.

85

18

Multiply together the two digits in the small squares, take the answer and then reverse the answer, subtracting the lower number from the higher number to obtain the number in the large square: 3 x 8 = 24, 24 reversed is 42, 42 – 24 = 18.

86

Outer ring = 7, inner ring = 3

In the outer ring all numbers are divisible by 7, in the second ring all numbers are divisible for 12, and in the inner ring all numbers are divisible by 3.

87

26

The numbers in the top left and bottom right diamonds are added together, then the numbers in the top right and bottom left diamonds are added together, and the difference between the two results is placed in the central diamond: 32 + 26 = 58, 15 + 17 = 32, 58 – 32 = 26.

88

144

Reading from left to right, the numbers in the circles are the result of multiplying together the numbers in the same position as each other in the three sets below, working from left to right, top to bottom each time: 8 x 9 x 2 = 144.

89

K

In the top row 6 + 8 = 14 (N), in the second 7 (11 – 4) + 12 (13 – 1) = 19 (S), in the third 4 (8 – 3 – 1) + 11 (15 – 3 – 1) = 15 (O), in the fourth 10 (13 – 3) + 1 (6 – 5) = 11 (K), and in the fifth 8 + 8 = 16 (P).

90

I

The sum total of the values of the letters in the middle row is deducted from the sum total of the values of the letters in the top row. The result is a two-digit number, the first digit being the value of the letter in the bottom left square, and the second digit being the value of the letter in the bottom right square: 18 (R) + 24 (X) + 4 (D) + 8 (H) = 54, 16 (P) + 7 (G) + 12 (L) = 35, 54 – 35 = 19, thus A (1) and I (9).

91

3

The fourth and fifth digits are read as a number. The first, second and third digits are the square of that number; and the sixth, seventh, eighth and ninth digits are the cube of that number: $17^3 = 4913$.

92

6

In each row, the sum total of the numbers in the central three squares is a two-digit number, the first digit is in the far left square, and the second digit is in the far right square: 13 + 6 + 20 = 39, 3 (left) and 9 (right).

93

6th June

The clock was correct on May 1st and gains one hour thereafter every six days, so at the (correct) time of 8:30 it showed: 9:30 on May 7th, 10:30 on May 13th, 11:30 on May 19th, 12:30 on May 25th, 1:30 on May 31st, and 2:30 on June 6th.

94

Left = 87, right = 147

In corresponding sectors of the pentagons, multiplying together the numbers in the top two pentagons produces the same total as adding the numbers in the bottom two pentagons: 14 x 12 = 168 – 81 = 87, 16 x 14 = 224 – 77 = 147.

95

631

Working from top to bottom, each number is the difference between the cubes of consecutive numbers in sequence from 20 working back to 14: $20^3 - 19^3 = 1141$, $19^3 - 18^3 = 1027$, $18^3 - 17^3 = 919$, $17^3 - 16^3 = 817$, $16^3 - 15^3 = 721$, $15^3 - 14^3 = 631$.

96

Top = 47, bottom = 44

A number in the inner circle is the difference between the two numbers in the sectors they touch in the middle circle. A number in the outer circle is the sum total of the numbers in the two sectors they touch in the middle circle plus the three sectors of the inner circle that touch those two sectors.

97

2	6	1	5	4	3
3	5	2	4	1	6
1	3	4	6	5	2
6	4	5	3	2	1
5	2	6	1	3	4
4	1	3	2	6	5

98

19345 and 367555

From top to bottom, multiply the first number by 13 to obtain the next number, deduct 14 to obtain the next, multiply by 15 to obtain the next, deduct 16 to obtain the next, multiply by 17 to obtain the next, deduct 18 to obtain the next, and multiply by 19 to obtain the next: 19363 – 18 = 19345 x 19 = 367555.

99

106

In each row, the sum total of the cubes of the numbers in the squares is equal to the sum total of the numbers in the circles: 6^3 = 216, 3^3 = 27, 216 + 27 = 243 – 137 = 106.

100

Top = 36, bottom = 87

The numbers in each sector in the top circle are one third those in the corresponding and diametrically opposite sector in the bottom circle.

101

5

Multiply the numbers in the top and right triangles, then divide the result by the number in the bottom triangle to obtain the number in the left triangle: 20 x 29 = 580 ÷ 116 = 5.

102

165

In each row, from left to right, multiply the first two numbers, then divide by 4 to obtain the third: 660 ÷ 4 = 165.

103

6498

They are cubes minus the squares of the numbers 12-19.

104

L

Each is diametrically opposite a number that is either the cube or the square of its value: (L) 12^3 = 1728.

105

11

The number is the difference between the total of all faces with an odd number of pips and the total of all faces with an even number of pips on the pairs of dice: 13 – 2 = 11.

106

16

In each row and column, the sum total of the four numbers in the divided corner squares equals the sum total of numbers in rectangles between them.

107

J

Moving from the top left box to the bottom right, then top right box, then bottom left box, and repeating, letters start at C and continue in alphabetical order, returning to A again once Z is reached; the order is from left to right in the top, middle, then bottom row.

108

48

The top left number is the result of multiplying together the two numbers at the bottom right; the second number down from the top left is the result of multiplying together the second and third numbers from the bottom right. Keep working in this way until 12 x 4 (=48) is reached.

109

4

Read each row from right to left. The result of first number multiplied by the second is a two-digit number, the digits being entered one per square: 9 x 6 = 54 (4, 5, 6, 9).

110

25

Multiply together the values of the letters in each quadrant, then multiply together the two digits of the total to obtain the number below: 11 (K) x 5 (E) = 55, 5 x 5 = 25.

111

31

In each column, the sum total of all letters with odd-numbered values is deducted from the sum total of all letters with even-numbered values: 1 (A) + 5 (E) + 15 (O) = 21, 10 (J) + 20 (T) + 22 (V) = 52, 52 – 21 = 31.

112

5

The first ten prime numbers, working backwards are 29 (10th), 23 (9th), 19 (8th), 17 (7th), etc. These are in pairs which, when added together, equal the sum given. Thus 3 (2nd) + 2 (1st) = 5.

113

922

Regard the contents of each circle as both a number and three separate digits. Multiply together the digits and add the result to the number to obtain the next in the sequence: 8 x 2 x 6 = 96 + 826 = 922.

114

Top = 68, bottom = 11.75

In each column, halve each number and add four to obtain the next down.

115

1712204

In each row, view the first two digits as a number (call it the first), view the second two digits as a number (call it the second), and view the last three digits as a number (call it the third). The third is the result of multiplying together the first and second numbers. Moving down each row from the top, first numbers increase by two and second numbers decrease by one. Thus 17 x 12 = 204.